Scott Foresman

Grade 5 Unit and End-of-Year Benchmark Tests

Teacher's Manual

Reading STREET

Grade 5

PEARSON

Glenview, Illinois • Boston, Massachusetts • Chandler, Arizona • Upper Saddle River, New Jersey

ISBN-13: 978-0-328-48470-6
ISBN-10:   0-328-48470-9

5 6 7 8 9 10 V011 19 18 17 16 15 14 13 12 11

Contents

OVERVIEW

Scott Foresman *Reading Street* provides a wide array of formal tests and classroom assessments to support instruction. Formal assessments include the following:

- Baseline Group Tests

- Weekly Selection Tests

- Fresh Reads for Differentiated Test Practice

- Unit and End-of-Year Benchmark Tests

This Teacher's Manual provides information for administering the Benchmark Tests, scoring the tests, and interpreting the results. Detailed information about other assessment materials and procedures may be found in the *Assessment Handbook*.

Description of the Benchmark Tests

In Grade 5, there are six Unit Benchmark Tests—one for each unit—and an End-of-Year Benchmark Test. The Unit Benchmark Tests are designed to measure student progress based on the comprehension skills and strategies, literary elements, vocabulary, writing conventions, and types of writing taught in each unit. The End-of-Year Benchmark Test measures skills covered in all six units. The Benchmark Tests offer an integrated approach to assessment by measuring all skills and strategies in relation to reading selections.

In addition, the Benchmark Tests are designed to provide practice in test-taking skills and to prepare students to take the Reading/Language Arts section of standardized tests, state tests, or teacher-made tests. The tests include both multiple-choice and constructed-response questions. They also include writing prompts that will help students prepare for state writing tests.

Each Unit Benchmark Test has these features:

- Each test has two components—Reading – Parts 1–3 and Writing – Part 4.

- Reading – Part 1 presents two selections in different genres. The genres of these selections, drawn from fiction and nonfiction, reflect genres taught in each unit.

- Each selection reflects the theme of the unit.

- Reading – Parts 1–3 contain forty multiple-choice questions and two constructed-response questions. These questions test reading comprehension, literary elements, critical thinking skills, vocabulary strategies, and writing conventions. Some of the items measure the ability to synthesize information and to compare and contrast across texts.

- Writing – Part 4 of each test presents a writing prompt based on one of the types of writing taught in the unit. These prompts are similar to those found in state writing tests.

The End-of-Year Benchmark Test follows the same design as the Unit Benchmark Tests, but it has more items. It measures selected skills from all six units taught during the year.

The Benchmark Tests are designed to assess student progress at the end of each unit and at the end of the school year. Passages and questions in the Unit Benchmark Tests become progressively more difficult from Unit 1 to Unit 6 to reflect the increasing sophistication of materials students are able to handle.

ADMINISTERING THE TESTS

The Benchmark Tests are designed for group administration. You may decide to administer each test in one sitting, or you may administer parts of the test in two or more sittings. (If you administer the test in two or more sittings, try to schedule the sittings on the same day or within a day of the previous sitting because some of the questions at the end of the test compare and contrast selections.)

These tests are also designed to give teachers the option of separating multiple-choice questions from the constructed-response questions. You may opt to have students skip the constructed-response questions in order to create an all multiple-choice test.

These tests are not intended to be timed. We recommend allowing ample time for all students to complete the tests at their own pace. However, for the purposes of scheduling, planning, and practicing timed-test situations, the chart below shows the number of items in each test part and the estimated amount of time required to complete each part.

Test Part	Number of Items	Estimated Time
Reading – Part 1 (Selection 1)	11 multiple-choice	20–25 minutes
	1 constructed-response	5 minutes
Reading – Part 1 (Selection 2)	11 multiple-choice	20–25 minutes
	1 constructed-response	5 minutes
Reading – Part 2 (Vocabulary)	10 multiple-choice	20 minutes
Reading – Part 3 (Writing Conventions) OPTIONAL	8 multiple-choice	15–20 minutes
Writing – Part 4 OPTIONAL	1 writing prompt	45 minutes

The End-of-Year Benchmark Test has longer passages, sixty multiple-choice items, two constructed-response items, and one writing prompt. To administer the End-of-Year Test, plan on about two hours for Reading – Parts 1–3 and forty-five minutes for Writing – Part 4.

Directions for Administering the Tests
Before you administer a test . . .

Review the test directions below and on pages T8–T9. Modify the directions as needed based on how you decide to administer each test. For Reading – Parts 1–3, students can mark their responses directly on their tests or on the Bubble Answer Sheets included for copy on pages T55–T56. In Writing – Part 4 of all the tests, students write compositions in response to a prompt. They write their compositions on the lined pages in their test booklets. You may wish to provide scrap paper that students can use to plan their writing. Only the writing in their test booklets will be scored.

When you are ready to administer a test . . .

Distribute a test to each student. Have students write their names on the front of their test booklets, their answer sheets, and on any additional sheets of paper they may use. Have students flip through the test as you point out and explain its key features. For example, point out directions, selection titles, selections, art, Go On and Stop symbols, multiple-choice questions with answer choices, constructed-response questions with lines for written responses, and the writing prompt with a checklist and two lined pages for the compositions. Allow time for students to ask any questions they may have about the test's contents before you begin the test.

Directions in **bold** type that follow are intended to be read aloud. Other directions are intended for your information only. For Reading – Part 1, modify the general directions as needed if you intend to skip the constructed-response questions. For Writing – Part 4, you may wish to modify directions about the amount of time suggested for the testing session to match the time allowed for your state's writing tests.

Directions for Reading – Part 1: Comprehension

In the first part of this test, you will read two selections and answer some questions about them. There are two types of questions: multiple-choice questions and questions that require you to write short answers.

If you are having students mark their answers to the multiple-choice questions directly on their tests, then say:

Mark your answers to the multiple-choice questions in your test. For each question, circle the letter that goes with the answer you choose. If you want to change your answer, completely erase the circle you made and circle a different letter. Do not make any other marks in your test.

If students are marking their answers to the multiple-choice questions on answer sheets, then say:

Mark your answers to the multiple-choice questions on your answer sheet. For each question, fill in the circle on your answer sheet that goes with the answer you choose. Fill in the circle completely and make your mark heavy and dark. If you want to change your answer, completely erase the mark you made and fill in a different circle. Do not make any other marks on your answer sheet.

For all students, say:

For Questions A and B, write your answers on the lines in your test. Think carefully and write your ideas as clearly as you can. Allow about five minutes to answer each of these questions.

Read the directions carefully. You can ask me to explain any directions you do not understand. Read the selections and the questions very carefully. You may look back at a selection as often as you like to help you answer the questions.

Answer the questions you are sure about first. If a question seems too difficult, skip it and go back to it later. Check each answer to make sure it is the best answer for the question asked.

Think positively. Some questions may seem hard, but others will be easy. Relax. Most people get nervous about tests. It's natural. Just do your best.

Continue with Reading Part 1: Comprehension until you come to a STOP sign at the end of Question B. When you have completed that question, put your pencils down, close your test booklets, and look up.

Tell students how much of the test they are expected to complete in this sitting and how much time they have to complete their work. Allow time for students to ask any questions about the directions. Then direct students to open their tests to a specified page and begin. You may wish to give students a break upon completion of this part of the test.

Directions for Reading – Part 2 and Optional Part 3

Read aloud the directions from the student book for Parts 2 and 3. Tell students how much time they have to complete their work for each part of the test. Point out the STOP sign at the end of each part and instruct students to put their pencils down and look up whenever they come to a STOP sign. That way, you can wait for all students to complete the section before moving on to the next part.

Directions for Writing – Part 4 (Optional)

For the last part of the test, you will do a writing exercise. The writing prompt in your test explains what you are going to write about and gives you some ideas for planning your writing. Before you begin writing, think about what you want to say and how you want to say it. You can use scrap paper to jot down your ideas.

After planning what you will write, write your composition on the two lined pages in your test. Be sure that your writing does what the prompt asks you to do. Only the writing in your test booklet will be scored.

Your writing may be about something that is real or make-believe, but remember, you are to write ONLY about the prompt in your test.

You may give your writing a title if you would like. However, a title is not required.

You may NOT use a dictionary. If you do not know how to spell a word, sound the word out and do the best you can.

You may either print or write in cursive. It is important to write as neatly as possible.

Your writing should be easy to read and should show that you can organize and express your thoughts clearly and completely.

I cannot read the prompt to you or help you plan what to write. You must read and plan yourself. Remember to read the prompt first and then plan what you will write.

You have a total of forty-five minutes to read, plan, and respond to your prompt. I will let you know when you have ten minutes left. (You may wish to modify the amount of time you allow for Writing – Part 4 to match the time allowed on your state's writing tests.)

If you finish early, please proofread your composition. Revise and edit the writing in your test. Use the questions in the checklist to help you check your composition.

Allow time for students to ask any questions about the directions. Then direct students to open their tests to the writing prompt page, read the prompt, plan their writing, and then write their compositions. Be sure to alert students when they have ten minutes left.

After testing . . .

Once students are finished testing, collect all test booklets and any answer sheets or scrap paper. Directions for scoring the tests begin on page T10. The answer keys begin on page T45. Evaluation charts (T29–T45) are provided along with a class record chart on page T43.

SCORING THE TESTS

The Benchmark Tests are intended to be scored by part—a total score for Reading – Parts 1–3 and a separate score for Writing – Part 4. To make scoring easier, copy and use the following charts as needed:

- the Unit Benchmark Test Evaluation Charts, beginning on page T29, for recording a student's individual scores on a Unit Benchmark Test;

- the End-of-Year Benchmark Test Evaluation Chart, on pages T41 and T42, for recording a student's individual scores on the End-of-Year Benchmark Test;

- the Class Record Chart, on page T43, for recording test scores for all students for all six units.

Answer keys for each test begin on page T45. In Reading – Part 1, there are two types of items: multiple-choice questions and constructed-response questions. These types of items are scored in slightly different ways, as explained below. In Writing – Part 4, each prompt is linked to one of four different types of writing: narrative, descriptive, expository, or persuasive. For each type of writing, there are four Writing Scoring Rubrics. Each rubric has a different point scale. Choose the rubric that most closely matches the rubric for your state's writing tests or the rubric you deem most appropriate for your students. Writing Scoring Rubrics begin on page T12.

Scoring Multiple-Choice Questions

Each multiple-choice question has four answer choices labeled A, B, C, D or F, G, H, J. Refer to the answer key for the test you are scoring and mark each multiple-choice question as either 1 (correct) or 0 (incorrect).

Scoring Constructed-Response Questions

Use the answer keys and the rubric on page T11 to help you score constructed-response questions. Award each constructed-response answer a score from 0 to 2 points, depending on how accurate and complete the response is. The answer keys provide abbreviated descriptions of top responses. Have an ideal top response in mind before you assess students' responses.

Constructed-Response Scoring Rubric

Points	Description
2	The response indicates a **full understanding** of the question's reading or critical thinking skill. The response is accurate and complete. Necessary support and/or examples are included, and the information is clearly text-based.
1	The response indicates a **partial understanding** of the question's reading or critical thinking skill. The response includes information that is essentially correct and text-based, but it is too general or too simplistic. Some of the support and/or examples may be incomplete or omitted.
0	The response is **inaccurate,** confused, and/or irrelevant, or the student has failed to respond to the task.

Scoring Writing – Part 4

To evaluate students' responses to a writing prompt, familiarize yourself with the writing prompt and review the Writing Scoring Rubrics on pages T12–T19. Identify the type of writing suggested in the writing prompt. (Types of writing for each prompt are identified in the answer keys that begin on page T45.) Then choose one of the four Writing Scoring Rubrics provided for that type of writing. Use the rubric to score each composition on a scale from 1 to 6, 1 to 5, 1 to 4, or 1 to 3.

Writing Scoring Rubrics: Narrative Writing

6-Point Scoring Rubric

6	5	4	3	2	1
narrative writing is well focused on the topic	narrative writing is focused on the topic	narrative writing is generally focused on the topic	narrative writing is generally focused but may stray from the topic	narrative writing is minimally related to the topic	narrative writing is not focused on the topic
contains clear ideas	most ideas are clear	ideas are generally clear	ideas may be somewhat unclear	ideas are often unclear	ideas are unclear
logically organized; uses transitions	logically organized; uses some transitions	logically organized with some lapses; has transitions	somewhat organized; may lack transitions	minimally organized; no transitions	unorganized; no transitions
voice is engaging; well suited to purpose and audience	voice comes through well; suited to purpose and audience	voice comes through occasionally; suited to purpose and audience	voice uneven; not always suited to purpose or audience	slight evidence of voice; little sense of purpose or audience	weak voice; no sense of purpose or audience
demonstrates varied, precise word choice	generally demonstrates varied, precise word choice	often demonstrates varied, precise word choice	word choice could be more varied, precise	poor choice of words; limited vocabulary	limited vocabulary
sentences are complete, fluent, and varied	most sentences are complete and varied	many sentences are complete and varied	some incomplete sentences; little variety	sentences are incomplete; show little or no variety	gross errors in sentence structure; no variety
shows excellent control of writing conventions	shows very good control of writing conventions	shows good control of writing conventions	shows fair control of writing conventions	shows frequent errors in writing conventions	shows many serious errors in writing conventions

5-Point Scoring Rubric

5	4	3	2	1
narrative writing is well focused on the topic	narrative writing is focused on the topic	narrative writing is generally focused on the topic	narrative writing strays from the topic	narrative writing is not focused on the topic
contains clear ideas	most ideas are clear	ideas are generally clear	many ideas are unclear	ideas are unclear
logically organized; uses transitions	logically organized; uses some transitions	logically organized with some lapses; transitions weak	little organization; few or no transitions	unorganized; no transitions
voice is engaging; well suited to purpose and audience	voice is fairly strong; suited to purpose and audience	voice comes through occasionally; may not suit purpose or audience	voice comes through rarely; poorly suited to purpose or audience	weak voice; no sense of audience or purpose
demonstrates varied, precise word choice	generally demonstrates varied, precise word choice	word choice could be more varied, precise	poor choice of words; limited vocabulary	choice of words very limited
sentences are complete, fluent, and varied	most sentences are complete and varied	many sentences are complete; generally varied	incomplete sentences; little variety	incomplete sentences; no variety
shows excellent control of writing conventions	shows very good control of writing conventions	shows fairly good control of writing conventions	shows frequent errors in writing conventions	shows many serious errors in writing conventions

Benchmark Test Teacher's Manual

Writing Scoring Rubrics: Narrative Writing

4-Point Scoring Rubric

4	3	2	1
narrative writing is well focused on the topic	narrative writing is focused on the topic	narrative writing may stray from the topic	narrative writing is not focused on the topic
contains clear ideas	most ideas are clear	some ideas may be unclear	ideas are unclear
logically organized; uses transitions	logically organized; uses some transitions	little organization; may be few or no transitions	unorganized; no transitions
voice is engaging; well suited to purpose and audience	voice is fairly strong; suited to purpose and audience	slight evidence of voice; may be poorly suited to purpose or audience	weak voice; no sense of audience or purpose
demonstrates varied, precise word choice	generally demonstrates varied, precise word choice	choice of words limited	choice of words very limited
sentences are complete, fluent, and varied	most sentences are complete and varied	many incomplete sentences; little variety	mostly incomplete sentences; no variety
shows excellent control of writing conventions	shows very good control of writing conventions	shows frequent errors in writing conventions	shows many serious errors in writing conventions

3-Point Scoring Rubric

3	2	1
narrative writing is well focused on the topic	narrative writing is generally focused on the topic	narrative writing is not focused on the topic
contains clear ideas	ideas are sometimes unclear	ideas are unclear
logically organized; uses transitions	logically organized with lapses; transitions need improvement	unorganized; no transitions
voice is engaging; well suited to purpose and audience	voice comes through fairly well; may not suit purpose or audience	weak voice; no sense of audience
demonstrates varied, precise word choice	word choice could be more varied, precise	choice of words very limited
sentences are complete, fluent, and varied	some sentences are complete and varied	incomplete sentences; no variety
shows excellent control of writing conventions	shows fair control of writing conventions	shows many serious errors in writing conventions

Writing Scoring Rubrics: Descriptive Writing

6-Point Scoring Rubric

6	5	4	3	2	1
descriptive writing is well focused on the topic	descriptive writing is focused on the topic	descriptive writing is generally focused on the topic	descriptive writing may stray from the topic	descriptive writing is minimally related to the topic	descriptive writing is not focused on the topic
contains clear ideas	most ideas are clear	ideas are generally clear	ideas may be somewhat unclear	ideas are often unclear	ideas are unclear
logically organized; uses transitions	logically organized; uses some transitions	logically organized with some lapses; has transitions	somewhat organized; may lack transitions	minimally organized; no transitions	unorganized; no transitions
voice is engaging; well suited to purpose and audience	voice comes through well; suited to purpose and audience	voice comes through occasionally; suited to purpose and audience	voice uneven; not always suited to purpose or audience	slight evidence of voice; little sense of purpose or audience	weak voice; no sense of purpose or audience
precise, vivid language paints strong pictures	generally demonstrates varied, precise word choice	often demonstrates varied, precise word choice	word choice could be more varied, precise	poor choice of words; limited vocabulary	limited vocabulary
sentences are complete, fluent, and varied	most sentences are complete and varied	many sentences are complete and varied	some incomplete sentences; little variety	sentences are incomplete; show little or no variety	gross errors in sentence structure; no variety
shows excellent control of writing conventions	shows very good control of writing conventions	shows good control of writing conventions	shows fair control of writing conventions	shows frequent errors in writing conventions	shows many serious errors in writing conventions

5-Point Scoring Rubric

5	4	3	2	1
descriptive writing is well focused on the topic	descriptive writing is focused on the topic	descriptive writing is generally focused on the topic	descriptive writing strays from the topic	descriptive writing is not focused on the topic
contains clear ideas	most ideas are clear	ideas are generally clear	many ideas are unclear	ideas are unclear
logically organized; uses transitions	logically organized; uses some transitions	logically organized with some lapses; transitions weak	little organization; few or no transitions	unorganized; no transitions
voice is engaging; well suited to purpose and audience	voice is fairly engaging; suited to purpose and audience	voice comes through occasionally; may not suit purpose or audience	voice comes through rarely; poorly suited to purpose or audience	weak voice; no sense of audience or purpose
demonstrates varied, precise word choice	generally demonstrates varied, precise word choice	word choice could be more varied, precise	poor word choice; limited vocabulary	word choice very limited
sentences are complete, fluent, and varied	most sentences are complete and varied	many sentences are complete; generally varied	incomplete sentences; little variety	incomplete sentences; no variety
shows excellent control of writing conventions	shows very good control of writing conventions	shows fairly good control of writing conventions	shows frequent errors in writing conventions	shows many serious errors in writing conventions

Writing Scoring Rubrics: Descriptive Writing

4-Point Scoring Rubric			
4	**3**	**2**	**1**
descriptive writing is well focused on the topic	descriptive writing is focused on the topic	descriptive writing may stray from the topic	descriptive writing is not focused on the topic
contains clear ideas	most ideas are clear	some ideas may be unclear	ideas are unclear
logically organized; uses transitions	logically organized; uses some transitions	little organization; may be few or no transitions	unorganized; no transitions
voice is engaging; well suited to purpose and audience	voice is fairly engaging; suited to purpose and audience	slight evidence of voice; may be poorly suited to audience or purpose	weak voice; no sense of audience or purpose
demonstrates varied, precise word choice	generally demonstrates varied, precise word choice	choice of words limited	word choice very limited
sentences are complete, fluent, and varied	most sentences are complete and varied	many incomplete sentences; little variety	mostly incomplete sentences; no variety
shows excellent control of writing conventions	shows very good control of writing conventions	shows frequent errors in writing conventions	shows many serious errors in writing conventions

3-Point Scoring Rubric		
3	**2**	**1**
descriptive writing is well focused on the topic	descriptive writing is generally focused on the topic	descriptive writing is not focused on the topic
contains clear ideas	ideas are sometimes unclear	ideas are unclear
logically organized; uses transitions	logically organized with lapses; transitions need improvement	unorganized; no transitions
voice is engaging; well suited to purpose and audience	voice comes through fairly well; may not suit purpose or audience	weak voice; no sense of purpose or audience
demonstrates varied, precise word choice	word choice could be more varied, precise	choice of words very limited
sentences are complete, fluent, and varied	some sentences are complete and varied	incomplete sentences; no variety
shows excellent control of writing conventions	shows fair control of writing conventions	shows many serious errors in writing conventions

Writing Scoring Rubrics: Expository Writing

6-Point Scoring Rubric

6	5	4	3	2	1
expository writing is well focused on the topic	expository writing is focused on the topic	expository writing is generally focused on the topic	expository writing may stray from the topic	expository writing is minimally related to the topic	expository writing is not focused on the topic
contains clear ideas	most ideas are clear	ideas are generally clear	ideas may be somewhat unclear	ideas are often unclear	ideas are unclear
logically organized; uses transitions	logically organized; uses some transitions	logically organized with some lapses; has transitions	little organization; may lack transitions	minimally organized; no transitions	unorganized; no transitions
voice is engaging; well suited to purpose and audience	voice comes through well; suited to purpose and audience	voice comes through occasionally; suited to purpose and audience	voice uneven; not always suited to purpose or audience	slight evidence of voice; little sense of purpose or audience	weak voice; no sense of purpose or audience
demonstrates varied, precise word choice	generally demonstrates varied, precise word choice	often demonstrates varied, precise word choice	word choice could be more varied, precise	poor choice of words; limited vocabulary	limited vocabulary
sentences are complete, fluent, and varied	most sentences are complete and varied	many sentences are complete and varied	some incomplete sentences; little variety	sentences are incomplete; show little or no variety	gross errors in sentence structure; no variety
shows excellent control of writing conventions	shows very good control of writing conventions	shows good control of writing conventions	shows fair control of writing conventions	shows frequent errors in writing conventions	shows many serious errors in writing conventions

5-Point Scoring Rubric

5	4	3	2	1
expository writing is well focused on the topic	expository writing is focused on the topic	expository writing is generally focused on the topic	expository writing strays from the topic	expository writing is not focused on the topic
contains clear ideas	most ideas are clear	ideas are generally clear	many ideas are unclear	ideas are unclear
logically organized; uses transitions	logically organized; uses some transitions	logically organized with some lapses; transitions weak	little organization; few or no transitions	unorganized; no transitions
voice is engaging; well suited to purpose and audience	voice is fairly engaging; suited to purpose and audience	voice comes through occasionally; may not suit purpose or audience	voice comes through rarely; poorly suited to purpose or audience	weak voice; no sense of audience or purpose
demonstrates varied, precise word choice	generally demonstrates varied, precise word choice	word choice could be more varied, precise	poor word choice; limited vocabulary	word choice very limited
sentences are complete, fluent, and varied	most sentences are complete and varied	many sentences are complete; generally varied	incomplete sentences; little variety	incomplete sentences; no variety
shows excellent control of writing conventions	shows very good control of writing conventions	shows fairly good control of writing conventions	shows frequent errors in writing conventions	shows many serious errors in writing conventions

Writing Scoring Rubrics: Expository Writing

4-Point Scoring Rubric

4	3	2	1
expository writing is well focused on the topic	expository writing is focused on the topic	expository writing may stray from the topic	expository writing is not focused on the topic
contains clear ideas	most ideas are clear	some ideas may be unclear	ideas are unclear
logically organized; uses transitions	logically organized; uses some transitions	little organization; may be few or no transitions	unorganized; no transitions
voice is engaging; well suited to purpose and audience	voice is fairly engaging; suited to purpose and audience	slight evidence of voice; may be poorly suited to audience or purpose	weak voice; no sense of audience or purpose
demonstrates varied, precise word choice	generally demonstrates varied, precise word choice	choice of words limited	word choice very limited
sentences are complete, fluent, and varied	most sentences are complete and varied	many incomplete sentences; little variety	mostly incomplete sentences; no variety
shows excellent control of writing conventions	shows very good control of writing conventions	shows frequent errors in writing conventions	shows many serious errors in writing conventions

3-Point Scoring Rubric

3	2	1
expository writing is well focused on the topic	expository writing is generally focused on the topic	expository writing is not focused on the topic
contains clear ideas	ideas are sometimes unclear	ideas are unclear
logically organized; uses transitions	logically organized with lapses; transitions need improvement	unorganized; no transitions
voice is engaging; well suited to purpose and audience	voice comes through fairly well; may not suit purpose or audience	weak voice; no sense of purpose or audience
demonstrates varied, precise word choice	word choice could be more varied, precise	choice of words very limited
sentences are complete, fluent, and varied	some sentences are complete and varied	incomplete sentences; no variety
shows excellent control of writing conventions	shows fair control of writing conventions	shows many serious errors in writing conventions

Writing Scoring Rubrics: Persuasive Writing

6-Point Scoring Rubric

6	5	4	3	2	1
persuasive writing is well focused on the topic	persuasive writing is focused on the topic	persuasive writing is generally focused on the topic	persuasive writing is generally focused but may stray from the topic	persuasive writing is minimally related to the topic	persuasive writing is not focused on the topic
contains clear ideas	most ideas are clear	ideas are generally clear	ideas may be somewhat unclear	ideas are often unclear	ideas are unclear
presents reasons in order; uses transitions	presents reasons in some order; uses some transitions	presents most reasons in order; has transitions	reasons may not be in proper order; may lack transitions	reasons are not in order; no transitions	reasons, if any, are not in order; no transitions
voice is engaging; well suited to purpose and audience	voice comes through well; suited to purpose and audience	voice comes through occasionally; suited to purpose and audience	voice uneven; not always suited to purpose or audience	slight evidence of voice; little sense of audience or purpose	weak voice; no sense of purpose or audience
demonstrates precise, persuasive wording	generally demonstrates precise, persuasive word choice	often demonstrates precise, persuasive word choice	word choice is not always precise or persuasive	poor choice of words; not very persuasive	limited vocabulary; fails to persuade
sentences are complete, fluent, and varied	most sentences are complete and varied	many sentences are complete and varied	some incomplete sentences; little variety	sentences are incomplete; show little or no variety	gross errors in sentence structure; no variety
shows excellent control of writing conventions	shows very good control of writing conventions	shows good control of writing conventions	shows fair control of writing conventions	shows frequent errors in writing conventions	shows many serious errors in writing conventions

5-Point Scoring Rubric

5	4	3	2	1
persuasive writing is well focused on the topic	persuasive writing is focused on the topic	persuasive writing is generally focused on the topic	persuasive writing strays from the topic	persuasive writing is not focused on the topic
contains clear ideas	most ideas are clear	ideas are generally clear	many ideas are unclear	ideas are unclear
presents reasons in order; uses transitions	presents reasons in some order; uses some transitions	presents most reasons in order; transitions weak	reasons are not in order; few or no transitions	reasons, if any, are not in order; no transitions
voice is engaging; well suited to purpose and audience	voice is fairly engaging; suited to purpose and audience	voice comes through occasionally; may not suit purpose or audience	voice comes through rarely; poorly suited to audience or purpose	weak voice; no sense of audience or purpose
demonstrates precise, persuasive wording	generally demonstrates precise, persuasive word choice	word choice could be more precise, persuasive	word choice limited; not persuasive	word choice very limited; fails to persuade
sentences are complete, fluent, and varied	most sentences are complete and varied	many sentences are complete; generally varied	incomplete sentences; little variety	incomplete sentences; no variety
shows excellent control of writing conventions	shows very good control of writing conventions	shows fairly good control of writing conventions	shows frequent errors in writing conventions	shows many serious errors in writing conventions

Writing Scoring Rubrics: Persuasive Writing

Writing Scoring Rubrics: Persuasive Writing

4-Point Scoring Rubric

4	3	2	1
persuasive writing is well focused on the topic	persuasive writing is focused on the topic	persuasive writing may stray from the topic	persuasive writing is not focused on the topic
contains clear ideas	most ideas are clear	some ideas may be unclear	ideas are unclear
presents reasons in order; uses transitions	presents reasons in some order; uses some transitions	reasons may not be in order; may be few or no transitions	reasons, if any, are not in order; no transitions
voice is engaging; well suited to purpose and audience	voice is fairly engaging; suited to purpose and audience	slight evidence of voice; may be poorly suited to purpose or audience	weak voice; no sense of audience or purpose
demonstrates precise, persuasive wording	generally demonstrates precise, persuasive word choice	choice of words limited; not very persuasive	word choice very limited; fails to persuade
sentences are complete, fluent, and varied	most sentences are complete and varied	many incomplete sentences; little variety	many incomplete sentences; no variety
shows excellent control of writing conventions	shows very good control of writing conventions	shows frequent errors in writing conventions	shows many serious errors in writing conventions

3-Point Scoring Rubric

3	2	1
persuasive writing is well focused on the topic	persuasive writing is generally focused on the topic	persuasive writing is not focused on the topic
contains clear ideas	ideas are sometimes unclear	ideas are unclear
logically organized; presents reasons in order	logically organized with lapses; presents most reasons in order	unorganized; reasons, if any, are not in order
voice is engaging; well suited to purpose and audience	voice comes through fairly well; may not suit audience or purpose	weak voice; no sense of audience or purpose
demonstrates precise, persuasive word choice	word choice could be more precise, persuasive	choice of words very limited; fails to persuade
sentences are complete, fluent, and varied	some sentences are complete and varied	incomplete sentences; no variety
shows excellent control of writing conventions	shows fair control of writing conventions	shows many serious errors in writing conventions

Using an Evaluation Chart

Use the Evaluation Charts beginning on page T29 to score the Unit Benchmark Tests and the End-of-Year Benchmark Test. To score one of these tests use the following procedure:

1. Make a copy of the appropriate Evaluation Chart for each student.

2. To score Reading – Parts 1–3, circle the score for each item on the Evaluation Chart. Multiple-choice questions are scored 0 (incorrect) or 1 (correct). Constructed-response questions are scored 0, 1, or 2 points. Use the answer key for the test you are scoring and the Constructed-Response Scoring Rubric on page T11 to help you score the Reading parts of the test.

3. Find the student's total score for Reading – Parts 1–3 by adding the individual scores for all items.

4. Use the formula on the Evaluation Chart to find the percentage score for Reading – Parts 1–3 by dividing the total *obtained* score by the total *possible* score and then multiplying the quotient by 100.

5. To score Writing – Part 4, identify the type of writing suggested in the prompt and choose one of the four Writing Scoring Rubrics for that type of writing. Read the student's writing and score each composition on a scale from 1 to 6, 1 to 5, 1 to 4, or 1 to 3.

6. Mark the student's Writing – Part 4 score on the Evaluation Chart. Add any notes or observations about the writing that may be helpful to you and the student in later instruction.

INTERPRETING TEST RESULTS

A student's score on a Benchmark Test provides only one look at the student's progress and should be interpreted in conjunction with other assessments and the teacher's observations. However, a low score on one or both parts of a Benchmark Test probably indicates a need for closer review of the student's performance and perhaps additional instruction.

Regrouping for Instruction

The Benchmark Tests can help you make regrouping decisions. In Grade 5 there are opportunities for regrouping at the end of Units 2, 3, 4, and 5. Depending on each student's progress, teachers may prefer to regroup more or less frequently.

Students who score 65% or below on the multiple-choice items of the Comprehension and Vocabulary sections of the Benchmark Tests and who typically demonstrate unsatisfactory work on assignments and in classroom discussions would benefit from being in the Strategic Intervention reading group for the next unit of instruction.

Students who score between 66% and 90% on the multiple-choice items of the Comprehension and Vocabulary sections of the Benchmark Tests and who meet other criteria, such as consistently satisfactory work on assignments and in classroom discussions, likely belong in the On-Level reading group for the next unit of instruction. Students in the low end of that range should be observed carefully and may need on-going assistance, extra instruction, and opportunities for further practice, just as students in the Strategic Intervention group do. Students in the upper end of that range should receive their instruction and practice with on-level materials, but they may need extra challenge and enrichment, just as students in the Advanced reading group do.

Students who score 91% or above on the multiple-choice items of the Comprehension and Vocabulary sections of the Benchmark Tests and who meet other criteria, such as consistently excellent performance on assigned paperwork and in classroom discussions, are capable of work in the Advanced reading group for the next unit of instruction. They should be given multiple opportunities to engage in enrichment activities and real-world investigations.

Further Analysis of Results

Each Reading (Parts 1–3) item on an Evaluation Chart is linked to a tested skill. By identifying which items the student answered incorrectly and referring to the list of tested skills, you may be able to determine specific skills or areas in which the student needs additional help. For example, if the student answers six questions incorrectly and several involve literary elements such as plot and character, you may want to plan additional instruction for the student in this area. While the Benchmark Tests do not provide sufficient context coverage of individual skills to be truly "diagnostic," students' performance patterns can often provide useful clues as to particular strengths and weaknesses.

Grading: For more information on how to use a writing assessment scale as an element in determining classroom grades, refer to the "Grading Writing" section of the *Assessment Handbook*.

ASSISTING ENGLISH LANGUAGE LEARNERS

While the Benchmark Tests provide teachers with a way to measure students' progress on a unit-by-unit basis, Benchmark Tests also provide an opportunity for teachers to help English language learners become familiar with the linguistic patterns and structures they will encounter while taking state tests. The format of the Benchmark Tests is similar to the format of the state tests, with similar direction lines, question stems, answer formats, and markings to "stop" and "go on."

Among assessment tools, standardized tests cause teachers of English language learners the most concern. State tests, considered "high stakes," may be used to evaluate the effectiveness of the curriculum, the teacher, or the instructional approach. They are used to evaluate students' overall progress. High-stakes tests are typically designed and normed for proficient speakers of English. By providing opportunities for English language learners to become familiar with the formats and language of the Benchmark Tests, teachers assist students in obtaining results that reflect students' learning of the content rather than their aptitude for comprehending test language and formats.

Teachers can use specific strategies to prepare English language learners for assessment. Using these strategies on the Benchmark Tests will increase students' comfort levels and success with assessment tools such as the state tests.

Testing Strategies for All English Language Learners

Provide Accommodations for Students' Success

Any accommodations appropriate for English language learners should address students' linguistic needs, either directly or indirectly. As you consider accommodations for students taking the Benchmark Tests, remember that when the state tests are given, no special accommodations are allowed. Therefore, as you make accommodations for English language learners, keep in mind that the ultimate goal is for these students to handle mainstream testing settings, terminology, and instruction. Any accommodations that you provide should be considered stepping stones to students' eventual successful encounter with mainstream testing conditions.

1. **Simplify and clarify directions.** Providing instructions in simplified formats can reduce the language load for English language learners and help them focus solely on the task and content for the specific question(s). A good rule of thumb is to match the language used with the test to the language used with instruction. Students benefit from your replacing complex English words with simpler English words that they are already familiar with or can grasp more easily. However, it is never appropriate to translate test directions into students' home languages. This practice will not benefit students when they encounter state tests. (*See below* **A Word of Caution.**) However, you may ask students to restate directions in their own words so you are sure they understand them.

2. **Provide a setting consistent with the instructional setting.** Administering tests in an alternate, smaller, even one-on-one, setting can allow for verbal scaffolding and provide English language learners with a setting that is comfortable and familiar to them. Be sure that the alternate setting is a setting with which students are familiar. Move students to mainstream testing settings when you feel they are ready.

3. **Consider timing.** Provide additional testing time and allow frequent or extended breaks during testing. On the Benchmark Tests, for example, students may benefit from a break between the two Comprehension passage/item sets and after the Comprehension and Vocabulary sections before moving on to the Writing Conventions section. The Writing sections are rigorous for students. Consider completing these portions on a different day or after a significant break. Keep in mind, however, that while this type of accommodation is one that is most often used for English language learners in mainstream classrooms, it is more important to be sure that students are receiving the necessary linguistic support in English.

4. **Provide dictionaries.** Allow the use of bilingual, word-for-word translation dictionaries as an accommodation for students who are able to use them effectively.

A Word of Caution: In providing accommodations to students, it is important not to compromise the intent of the assessment. It is never appropriate to translate into students' native languages or read aloud in English selections and questions. These practices alter the constructs of the assessments. The reading comprehension assessments, for example, are designed to measure both word recognition and understanding, so translating or reading the selections to students actually changes the intent of the tests.

Following the administration of the assessments, it is important to note which accommodations were used for English language learners and to interpret scores with that information in mind. As students progress in their English language skills and become more comfortable with testing, it is important to reconsider accommodations that were provided on previous tests.

Familiarize Students with Academic Language and Test Language

The Benchmark Tests use routine terminology and formats that are designed to mirror the experience of taking state tests. Helping students improve their understanding and use of academic language is an essential way to prepare students for assessment. The practice of "teaching to the test" is often criticized—and rightfully so—but helping English language learners understand the language and formats of tests and other assessment instruments levels the playing field for these students, allowing them to demonstrate what they've learned about the content, rather than struggling with the test language and formats. All students, but especially English language learners, must be taught test-taking strategies and must build background about the language and procedures of taking tests. **What strategies can you explicitly offer to students to prepare for assessment?**

1. Focus on Academic English and Meaningful Oral Language Experiences
Many English language learners may quickly master *social* English, the conversational language skills and conventions used in everyday interactions with classmates. These same learners, however, frequently encounter difficulty with the *academic* English found on formal assessments. Students may also have gaps in understanding between oral and written English. The structure of academic English is complex, e.g., fiction and nonfiction text structures, paragraph organization, and syntax, including prepositional phrases, introductory clauses, and pronoun references. There are structural analysis constraints at the word, sentence, paragraph, and text levels.

Development of academic language is one of the primary sources of difficulty for English language learners at all ages and grades, while also being fundamental to all students' success. The vocabulary of academic English consists of specialized meanings of common words, abstract concepts, multiple-meaning words, and words based on Latin and Greek roots. As students read test passages, they may encounter unfamiliar topics and concepts. Recognize that it takes years for students to master academic English, but that you can help them make progress on the way. Highlight and discuss routinely the *academic* language, vocabulary, syntax, and narrative and expository text structures encountered in textbooks and trade books. Remember that academic English is not another name for "standard English." Academic English is the special form of English that is used in the classroom and in written texts. The grammatical constructions, words, and rhetorical conventions are not often used in everyday spoken language. The home language does *not* have to be English in order for students to benefit from experiences in using academic language. If it proves helpful, students may be encouraged to connect what they know in their home languages to what they are learning about academic English.

Provide students with experiences with academic language by reading to them and discussing readings, instructional activities, and experiences. Draw students into instructional conversations focused on the language they encounter in their school texts and other materials to show students how language works. Provide students with ample opportunities to use the language of texts—and tests—in speaking and in writing. Provide regular opportunities for meaningful oral language experiences in which English language learners participate in discussion of important topics and perform the activities required on tests, such as explaining, describing, comparing, and stating and supporting opinions. Encourage them to use vocabulary that will support academic language development in increased opportunities for structured academic talk.

2. Focus on Test Directions

Help students understand phrases such as "make heavy dark marks" and "fill the circle completely" that are often used in test directions. When possible, model tasks

- **Make heavy dark marks that fill the circle completely.**

- **If you erase a grid circle, do not redraw it.**

- **Do not make any stray marks on this answer sheet.**

and provide verbal directions in simpler, more common English words. Be explicit in your teaching, using the following examples as a guide.

For the directions above, talk about the word *heavy* and its different meanings. Be sure students understand that here it means "dark." Explain that a *grid circle* is simply a "circle," *redraw* means "draw again," and *stray marks* means "marks in other places." Model and gesture how to follow the directions: *I use this answer sheet, or page. I find the number of the question in the booklet, or book, and I match the number in the booklet to the number on the sheet, or page, like this. Then I find the circle for the letter of the correct answer and make it all dark, or black, with my pencil. I do not make other marks on the page.* Be sure students can fill in the test form clearly and neatly.

3. Focus on Terminology and Strategies

Think about terms that will make the most sense to students as you teach. Instead of using the words *directions, test,* and *fill,* for example, you might use common cognates such as *instructions, exam,* and *mark,* which translate to most Romance languages (i.e., in Spanish: *instrucciones, examen,* and *marca*). However, move students to the original test words as soon as possible.

Pre-teach the "language of tests" encountered in directions and test items, including:

> Question words, such as: *who, what, which, where, when, why, how,* and *what kind*
>
> Emphasis words, such as: *best, better, first, last, not, except, probably, major, main, mainly, both, neither, either, same, different, begin, end, most, mostly,* and *least*
>
> Action words, such as: *explain, describe, compare,* and *discuss*

Words such as *both* and *not* may seem simple, but their uses in test questions often prove otherwise. English language learners need help in seeing how such words frame and constrain ideas expressed in sentences in which they appear.

Throughout the year, students need robust vocabulary instruction in English for additional common test words and phrases such as *test form, test booklet, answer sheet, mark the space, best describes, author, reader, purpose, paragraph, selection, article, passage, research, composition, writing prompt, details, events, results, according to, alike, opposite of, clue word, homonym, statements of fact and opinion, include, occur, present in, represent, resolve, valid comparison, important generalization, base your answer on,* and *support your answer.* Examine the tests for other words and phrases that are important for students to learn.

Familiarize students with basic test formats such as the lettering of multiple-choice options, underlining of words, cloze sentences, and writing-prompt boxes, so that they develop skills in locating key information. Use released tests or models of tests, providing students with plenty of practice in test formats. Be explicit in your instruction, using the following examples as a guide.

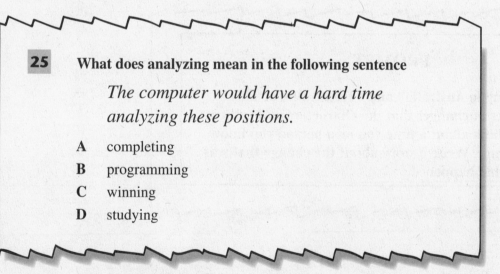

> **25**   **What does analyzing mean in the following sentence**
>
> *The computer would have a hard time analyzing these positions.*
>
> A   completing
> B   programming
> C   winning
> D   studying

Explain the test format: *Sometimes, test questions have words that are italicized. That means the words should stand out; the print looks different from other words in the question. I pay special attention to those words. Questions ask about these words.*

Use this entry from a dictionary to answer Number 20.

> **face** \fās\ *verb* **1.** to meet in a competition **2.** to recognize and deal with **3.** to cover the front of a surface **4.** to turn in a particular direction

29 Which definition does *face* have in the following sentence?

They knew they would face winds up to 100 miles per hour.

A   Definition 1

B   Definition 2

C   Definition 3

D   Definition 4

Explain the test format: *Some test questions use a dictionary entry, or the definitions or meanings of a word, to ask me what a word in the selection means. The word is italicized in the question. Some words have different meanings. The numbers in the dictionary entry show the different meanings of the word. I need to choose the right meaning. The correct answer is the meaning of the word as it is used in the sentence taken from the selection.* Model how to complete this type of question.

PROMPT

Both "Adapting in Australia" and "Take a Bite of This" tell about types of changes that the characters and subjects experience. Think about a time you or a person you know needed to change. Write a story about the change that was needed and what happened.

Explain the test format: *Some tests ask me to write a composition or story. At the top of the page is an instruction box, or writing prompt. First I read the instructions in the box to learn what to write about. The next two pages have lines for me to write on.* Explain also the "Checklist for Writers" box. *These are questions I read to myself and answer as I check over my writing to make sure it's just the way I want it.*

Model test-taking strategies for students. Help them use their emerging familiarity with vocabulary words and basic language structures in English to select the best answer and eliminate multiple-choice options. Teach students the logic of test questions. Show students, for example, that the question "Which of the following is *not* a sentence?" entails that all of the listed options except one *are* sentences. Be sure to teach students the types of reading comprehension questions they may encounter on tests. Use released test items or models of test items to provide students with plenty of practice in question types and the test-taking strategies you have taught them. Be explicit in your instruction, using the following examples as a guide.

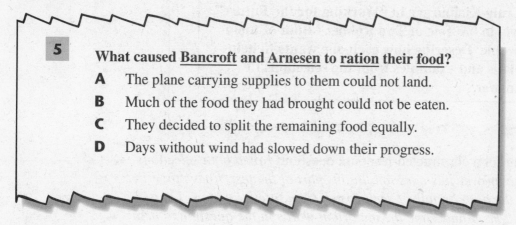

5 **What caused <u>Bancroft</u> and <u>Arnesen</u> to <u>ration</u> their <u>food</u>?**

 A The plane carrying supplies to them could not land.

 B Much of the food they had brought could not be eaten.

 C They decided to split the remaining food equally.

 D Days without wind had slowed down their progress.

Model a test-taking strategy for students—underlining key words in the question: *I read the whole selection carefully before I try to answer the questions. What if I can't remember something? Do I guess? No. I can make lines under the important words in the question. Then I can search for these words in the selection. I can read that part of the selection again. This will help me find the correct answer.*

9 **Which of the following contains a statement of opinion?**

 C Kielburger grew up in Canada.

 B Kielburger has traveled to more than 40 countries.

 C Kielburger believes that education can help people get out of poverty.

 D The organization started by Kielburger has built many schools around the world.

Model a test-taking strategy for students—eliminating incorrect multiple-choice options: *I read the whole selection carefully before I try to answer the questions. This question asks about an opinion. What is the difference between a statement of fact and a statement of opinion? A statement of fact can be proven true or false. A statement of opinion shows what someone feels or thinks about something. Now I read the answer choices. I try to find three answers that are not correct; they are statements of facts, not opinions. I look for opinion words. What are they? Words that show how someone feels or thinks.* Good examples are "wonderful," "great" "amazing," and statements such as "I believe." *Does the first answer have an opinion word? No, it is a fact, so I do not choose this answer.* Continue to model eliminating incorrect multiple-choice options. *The third answer is the correct answer. It has the statement, "Kielburger believes . . . " That shows his opinion, or what he thinks about education.*

PROMPT

Think about Craig <u>Kielburger</u> in "Working for the Future" and about Olivia in <u>"A Tale of Two Robots."</u> <u>Both</u> of them want to help people. <u>Describe how</u> each one wants to help people. Use details and examples from the selections to explain your answer.

Explain how to prepare for a constructed-response question: *I read both selections carefully before I try to answer this question. In this part of the test, I have to write. I read the question in the box carefully. I see two selection titles so I know I must think about both selections. I underline the important words in the question to help me understand what it is asking me to do—Kielburger, Olivia, Both, want, to help people, Describe how. From the word "Both" I know I need to write about both people, one from each selection. The question says to "use details or examples from the selections to explain my answer." What does that mean? So, I must give information from the selections that describes, or tells, how Kielburger and Olivia want to help people. I can read parts of both selections again to remember how they want to help people, using the important words in the question to help me. First I will write about Kielburger from "Working for the Future," and then I will write about Olivia from "A Tale of Two Robots."*

Model for students how to read the test itself. Proficient English readers may benefit from strategies such as reading the test question and answer options first and then skimming the passage to find information that will help them select the correct answer to the question. English language learners are not served well by this option. They need to read and understand the passage carefully and then consider how to answer the questions asked. Model this type of test-taking strategy for students as you think aloud and explain the process.

Summarize test formats and strategies for students. Consider making a T-chart to show examples of the question types that students may find on tests. If your T-chart is large enough to be a wall chart, include examples of each type of item from released tests and model tests on the chart. Explain what the structures are and what they ask test-takers to do (or ask students to explain as you teach various strategies).

Evaluation Chart: Grade 5 – Unit 1 Benchmark Test

Student Name _____ **Date** _____

Item	Tested Skill	Item Type*	Score (circle one)		
Reading – Parts 1–3					
Reading – Part 1: Comprehension					
1.	Literary elements: character	I	0	1	
2.	Cause and effect	I	0	1	
3.	Cause and effect	I	0	1	
4.	Literary elements: character	L	0	1	
5.	Literary elements: character	I	0	1	
6.	Author's purpose	C	0	1	
7.	Draw conclusions	I	0	1	
8.	Sequence	L	0	1	
9.	Compare and contrast	C	0	1	
10.	Sequence	I	0	1	
11.	Literary elements: theme	C	0	1	
A.	Constructed-response text-to-text connection		0	1	2
12.	Literary elements: character	I	0	1	
13.	Draw conclusions	I	0	1	
14.	Draw conclusions	I	0	1	
15.	Cause and effect	I	0	1	
16.	Literary elements: setting	L	0	1	
17.	Sequence	L	0	1	
18.	Cause and effect	L	0	1	
19.	Literary elements: character	C	0	1	
20.	Literary elements: theme	C	0	1	
21.	Author's purpose	I	0	1	
22.	Literary elements: character	I	0	1	
B.	Constructed-response text-to-text connection		0	1	2
Reading – Part 2: Vocabulary					
23.	Context clues: homonyms		0	1	
24.	Context clues: antonyms		0	1	
25.	Word structure: suffixes		0	1	
26.	Word structure: suffixes		0	1	
27.	Context clues: multiple-meaning words		0	1	
28.	Context clues: homonyms		0	1	
29.	Context clues: antonyms		0	1	

- - - - - - - - - - **Evaluation Chart: Grade 5 – Unit 1 Benchmark Test** - - - - - - - - - -

Reading – Part 2: Vocabulary (continued)

30.	Word structure: suffixes	0	1
31.	Context clues: multiple-meaning words	0	1
32.	Context clues: unfamiliar words	0	1
Student's Regrouping Multiple-Choice Score/Total Possible Score		_____ /32	

Reading – Part 3: Grammar, Usage, Mechanics

33.	Declarative sentences	0	1
34.	Interrogative sentences	0	1
35.	Imperative sentences	0	1
36.	Subjects and predicates	0	1
37.	Subjects and predicates	0	1
38.	Complex sentences	0	1
39.	Compound sentences	0	1
40.	Proper nouns	0	1
Student's Reading Total Score/Total Possible Score		_____ /44	

*L = literal   I = inferential   C = critical analysis

Regrouping (Reading — Parts 1–2) percentage: _____ ÷ 32 = _____ × 100 = _____%

                                  (student's score)   (percentage score)

Reading — Parts 1–3 percentage score: _____ ÷ 44 = _____ × 100 = _____%

                              (student's total score)   (percentage score)

Writing – Part 4

Writing Score (complete one) _____ /6   _____ /5   _____ /4   _____ /3

Notes/Observations:

Evaluation Chart: Grade 5 – Unit 2 Benchmark Test

Student Name _____ Date _____

Reading – Parts 1–3

Item	Tested Skill	Item Type*	Score (circle one)
Reading – Part 1: Comprehension			
1.	Sequence	L	0 1
2.	Sequence	C	0 1
3.	Sequence	I	0 1
4.	Draw conclusions	I	0 1
5.	Compare and contrast	I	0 1
6.	Compare and contrast	I	0 1
7.	Fact and opinion	C	0 1
8.	Generalize	I	0 1
9.	Cause and effect	I	0 1
10.	Author's purpose	C	0 1
11.	Compare and contrast	I	0 1
A.	Constructed-response text-to-self connection		0 1 2
12.	Sequence	L	0 1
13.	Sequence	L	0 1
14.	Compare and contrast	L	0 1
15.	Compare and contrast	L	0 1
16.	Draw conclusions	I	0 1
17.	Compare and contrast	I	0 1
18.	Literary elements: character	I	0 1
19.	Literary elements: setting	I	0 1
20.	Author's purpose	C	0 1
21.	Literary elements: theme	I	0 1
22.	Literary elements: plot	C	0 1
B.	Constructed-response text-to-text connection		0 1 2
Reading – Part 2: Vocabulary			
23.	Word structure: prefixes		0 1
24.	Word structure: prefixes		0 1
25.	Context clues: unfamiliar words		0 1
26.	Context clues: unfamiliar words		0 1
27.	Dictionary/glossary: multiple-meaning words		0 1
28.	Dictionary/glossary: unknown words		0 1
29.	Context clues: synonyms		0 1

Reading – Part 2: Vocabulary (continued)			
30.	Word structure: prefixes	0	1
31.	Dictionary/glossary: unfamiliar words	0	1
32.	Context clues: unfamiliar words	0	1
Student's Regrouping Multiple-Choice Score/Total Possible Score		_____	**/32**
Reading – Part 3: Writing Conventions			
33.	Regular and irregular plural nouns	0	1
34.	Regular and irregular plural nouns	0	1
35.	Regular and irregular plural nouns	0	1
36.	Subject/verb agreement	0	1
37.	Abbreviations and titles	0	1
38.	Common and proper nouns	0	1
39.	Common and proper nouns	0	1
40.	Main and helping verbs	0	1
Student's Reading Total Score/Total Possible Score		_____	**/44**

*L = literal   I = inferential   C = critical analysis

Regrouping (Reading — Parts 1–2) percentage: _____ ÷ 32 = _____ × 100 = _____%
                                                                    (student's score)   (percentage score)

Reading — Parts 1–3 percentage score: _____ ÷ 44 = _____ × 100 = _____%
                                                            (student's total score)   (percentage score)

Writing – Part 4

Writing Score (complete one) _____/6 _____/5 _____/4 _____/3

Notes/Observations:

Evaluation Chart: Grade 5 – Unit 3 Benchmark Test

Student Name _____ **Date** _____

Item	Tested Skill	Item Type*	Score (circle one)
Reading – Parts 1–3			
Reading – Part 1: Comprehension			
1.	Author's purpose	C	0 1
2.	Main idea and details	I	0 1
3.	Compare and contrast	I	0 1
4.	Author's purpose	I	0 1
5.	Fact and opinion	C	0 1
6.	Fact and opinion	C	0 1
7.	Main idea and details	L	0 1
8.	Draw conclusions	I	0 1
9.	Fact and opinion	C	0 1
10.	Main idea and details	L	0 1
11.	Generalize	I	0 1
A.	Constructed-response text-to-world connection		0 1 2
12.	Compare and contrast	L	0 1
13.	Main idea and details	I	0 1
14.	Cause and effect	I	0 1
15.	Draw conclusions	I	0 1
16.	Compare and contrast	L	0 1
17.	Fact and opinion	C	0 1
18.	Main idea and details	I	0 1
19.	Fact and opinion	C	0 1
20.	Sequence	L	0 1
21.	Author's purpose	C	0 1
22.	Generalize	I	0 1
B.	Constructed-response text-to-text connection		0 1 2
Reading – Part 2: Vocabulary			
23.	Context clues: homonyms		0 1
24.	Context clues: multiple-meaning words		0 1
25.	Context clues: antonyms		0 1
26.	Context clues: homonyms		0 1
27.	Context clues: multiple-meaning words		0 1
28.	Word structure: prefixes		0 1
29.	Context clues: multiple-meaning words		0 1

Reading – Part 2: Vocabulary (continued)			
30.	Context clues: multiple-meaning words	0	1
31.	Word structure: prefixes	0	1
32.	Context clues: homonyms	0	1
Student's Regrouping Multiple-Choice Score/Total Possible Score		_____	**/32**
Reading – Part 3: Writing Conventions			
33.	Principal parts of irregular verbs	0	1
34.	Past, present, and future tenses	0	1
35.	Past, present, and future tenses	0	1
36.	Troublesome verbs	0	1
37.	Troublesome verbs	0	1
38.	Past, present, and future tenses	0	1
39.	Prepositions and prepositional phrases	0	1
40.	Past, present, and future tenses	0	1
Student's Reading Total Score/Total Possible Score		_____	**/44**

*L = literal   I = inferential   C = critical analysis

Regrouping (Reading — Parts 1–2) percentage: _____ ÷ 32 = _____ × 100 = _____%
$\qquad\qquad\qquad$ (student's score) $\qquad\qquad\qquad\qquad\qquad$ (percentage score)

Reading — Parts 1–3 percentage score: _____ ÷ 44 = _____ × 100 = _____%
$\qquad\qquad\qquad$ (student's total score) $\qquad\qquad\qquad\qquad\qquad$ (percentage score)

Writing – Part 4

Writing Score (complete one) _____/6 _____/5 _____/4 _____/3

Notes/Observations:

Evaluation Chart: Grade 5 – Unit 4 Benchmark Test

Student Name _____   Date _____

Reading – Parts 1–3			
Item	**Tested Skill**	**Item Type***	**Score** (circle one)
Reading – Part 1: Comprehension			
1.	Cause and effect	L	0 1
2.	Draw conclusions	I	0 1
3.	Sequence	L	0 1
4.	Author's purpose	C	0 1
5.	Generalize	C	0 1
6.	Draw conclusions	I	0 1
7.	Generalize	C	0 1
8.	Generalize	I	0 1
9.	Draw conclusions	C	0 1
10.	Draw conclusions	I	0 1
11.	Author's purpose	C	0 1
A.	Constructed-response text-to-text connection		0 1 2
12.	Author's purpose	C	0 1
13.	Main idea and details	C	0 1
14.	Fact and opinion	C	0 1
15.	Compare and contrast	I	0 1
16.	Cause and effect	I	0 1
17.	Generalize	C	0 1
18.	Main idea and details	I	0 1
19.	Fact and opinion	C	0 1
20.	Draw conclusions	L	0 1
21.	Draw conclusions	I	0 1
22.	Generalize	I	0 1
B.	Constructed-response text-to-text connection		0 1 2
Reading – Part 2: Vocabulary			
23.	Word structure: suffixes		0 1
24.	Word structure: suffixes		0 1
25.	Context clues: synonyms		0 1
26.	Context clues: synonyms		0 1
27.	Word structure: suffixes		0 1
28.	Context clues: synonyms		0 1
29.	Context clues: unfamiliar words		0 1

Reading – Part 2: Vocabulary (continued)			
30.	Context clues: unfamiliar words	0	1
31.	Context clues: synonyms	0	1
32.	Context clues: synonyms	0	1
Student's Regrouping Multiple-Choice Score/Total Possible Score _____ /32			
Reading – Part 3: Writing Conventions			
33.	Using *Who* and *Whom*	0	1
34.	Indefinite pronouns	0	1
35.	Pronouns	0	1
36.	Pronouns	0	1
37.	Pronouns	0	1
38.	Reflexive pronouns	0	1
39.	Pronouns	0	1
40.	Pronouns	0	1
Student's Reading Total Score/Total Possible Score _____ /44			

*L = literal   I = inferential   C = critical analysis

Regrouping (Reading — Parts 1–2) percentage: _____ ÷ 32 = _____ × 100 = _____ %
(student's score)   (percentage score)

Reading — Parts 1–3 percentage score: _____ ÷ 44 = _____ × 100 = _____ %
(student's total score)   (percentage score)

Writing – Part 4

Writing Score (complete one) _____ /6 _____ /5 _____ /4 _____ /3

Notes/Observations:

Student Name _____ Date _____

Item	Tested Skill	Item Type*	Score (circle one)
Reading – Parts 1–3			
Reading – Part 1: Comprehension			
1.	Author's purpose	C	0 1
2.	Draw conclusions	C	0 1
3.	Cause and effect	L	0 1
4.	Cause and effect	L	0 1
5.	Fact and opinion	C	0 1
6.	Author's purpose	C	0 1
7.	Draw conclusions	C	0 1
8.	Draw conclusions	I	0 1
9.	Main idea and details	I	0 1
10.	Graphic sources	I	0 1
11.	Graphic sources	C	0 1
A.	Constructed-response text-to-world connection		0 1 2
12.	Graphic sources	C	0 1
13.	Graphic sources	C	0 1
14.	Main idea and details	I	0 1
15.	Author's purpose	C	0 1
16.	Compare and contrast	I	0 1
17.	Cause and effect	L	0 1
18.	Generalize	I	0 1
19.	Draw conclusions	I	0 1
20.	Main idea and details	C	0 1
21.	Sequence	L	0 1
22.	Author's purpose	C	0 1
B.	Constructed-response text-to-text connection		0 1 2
Reading – Part 2: Vocabulary			
23.	Word structure: prefixes		0 1
24.	Word structure: prefixes		0 1
25.	Word structure: prefixes		0 1
26.	Context clues: unfamiliar words		0 1
27.	Word structure: prefixes		0 1
28.	Word structure: prefixes		0 1
29.	Context clues: unfamiliar words		0 1

Reading – Part 2: Vocabulary (continued)			
30.	Context clues: multiple-meaning words	0	1
31.	Word structure: Greek and Latin roots	0	1
32.	Word structure: suffixes	0	1
Student's Regrouping Multiple-Choice Score/Total Possible Score _____ /32			
Reading – Part 3: Writing Conventions			
33.	Adverbs	0	1
34.	Adjectives	0	1
35.	Adjectives	0	1
36.	Adverbs	0	1
37.	Comparative and superlative adjectives	0	1
38.	Comparative and superlative adjectives	0	1
39.	Comparative and superlative adjectives	0	1
40.	Comparative and superlative adjectives	0	1
Student's Reading Total Score/Total Possible Score _____ /44			

*L = literal   I = inferential   C = critical analysis

Regrouping (Reading — Parts 1–2) percentage: _____ ÷ 32 = _____ × 100 = _____%

(student's score) (percentage score)

Reading — Parts 1–3 percentage score: _____ ÷ 44 = _____ × 100 = _____%

(student's total score) (percentage score)

Writing – Part 4
Writing Score (complete one) _____ /6 _____ /5 _____ /4 _____ /3
Notes/Observations:

Evaluation Chart: Grade 5 – Unit 6 Benchmark Test

Student Name _____ Date _____

Reading – Parts 1–3			
Item	**Tested Skill**	**Item Type***	**Score** (circle one)
Reading – Part 1: Comprehension			
1.	Sequence	I	0 1
2.	Sequence	I	0 1
3.	Fact and opinion	C	0 1
4.	Compare and contrast	L	0 1
5.	Draw conclusions	I	0 1
6.	Cause and effect	I	0 1
7.	Draw conclusions	I	0 1
8.	Draw conclusions	I	0 1
9.	Main idea and details	I	0 1
10.	Main idea and details	C	0 1
11.	Author's purpose	C	0 1
A.	Constructed-response text-to-world connection		0 1 2
12.	Sequence	L	0 1
13.	Draw conclusions	I	0 1
14.	Generalize	C	0 1
15.	Draw conclusions	I	0 1
16.	Literary elements: character	I	0 1
17.	Literary elements: plot	I	0 1
18.	Literary elements: plot	I	0 1
19.	Draw conclusions	I	0 1
20.	Sequence	I	0 1
21.	Author's purpose	C	0 1
22.	Literary elements: theme	I	0 1
B.	Constructed-response text-to-text connection		0 1 2
Reading – Part 2: Vocabulary			
23.	Word structure: suffixes		0 1
24.	Word structure: suffixes		0 1
25.	Context clues: unfamiliar words		0 1
26.	Dictionary/glossary: unfamiliar words		0 1
27.	Word structure: suffixes		0 1
28.	Word structure: suffixes		0 1
29.	Context clues: homonyms		0 1

Reading – Part 2: Vocabulary (continued)			
30.	Dictionary/glossary: unfamiliar words	0	1
31.	Word structure: suffixes	0	1
32.	Dictionary/glossary: unfamiliar words	0	1
Student's Regrouping Multiple-Choice Score/Total Possible Score		_____	/32
Reading – Part 3: Writing Conventions			
33.	Quotation marks	0	1
34.	Commas	0	1
35.	Commas	0	1
36.	Punctuation	0	1
37.	Commas	0	1
38.	Modifiers	0	1
39.	Commas	0	1
40.	Modifiers	0	1
Student's Reading Total Score/Total Possible Score		_____	/44

*L = literal I = inferential C = critical analysis

Regrouping (Reading — Parts 1–2) percentage: _____ ÷ 32 = _____ × 100 = _____%
(student's score) (percentage score)

Reading — Parts 1–3 percentage score: _____ ÷ 44 = _____ × 100 = _____%
(student's total score) (percentage score)

Writing – Part 4

Writing Score (complete one) _____/6 _____/5 _____/4 _____/3

Notes/Observations:

Evaluation Chart: Grade 5 – End-of-Year Benchmark Test

Student Name _____ Date _____

Reading – Parts 1–3

	Tested Skill	Item Type*	Score (circle one)	Item	Tested Skill	Item Type*	Score (circle one)
Reading – Part 1: Comprehension				27.	Compare and contrast	I	0 1
1.	Sequence	L	0 1	28.	Generalize	I	0 1
2.	Draw conclusions	I	0 1	29.	Fact and opinion	C	0 1
3.	Cause and effect	L	0 1	30.	Main idea and details	I	0 1
4.	Fact and opinion	C	0 1	31.	Graphic sources	C	0 1
5.	Draw conclusions	I	0 1	32.	Main idea and details	I	0 1
6.	Generalize	I	0 1	33.	Author's purpose	C	0 1
7.	Main idea and details	I	0 1	B.	Constructed-response text-to-text connection		0 1 2
8.	Compare and contrast	I	0 1	**Reading – Part 2: Vocabulary**			
9.	Main idea and details	I	0 1	34.	Word structure: prefixes		0 1
10.	Graphic sources	C	0 1	35.	Context clues: unfamiliar words		0 1
11.	Author's purpose	C	0 1	36.	Context clues: synonyms		0 1
12.	Sequence	I	0 1	37.	Dictionary/glossary: multiple-meaning words		0 1
13.	Literary elements: character	I	0 1	38.	Dictionary/glossary: multiple-meaning words		0 1
14.	Literary elements: plot	C	0 1	39.	Context clues: unfamiliar words		0 1
15.	Main idea and details	I	0 1	40.	Context clues: synonyms		0 1
16.	Literary elements: theme	C	0 1	41.	Word structure: suffixes		0 1
17.	Compare and contrast	I	0 1	42.	Dictionary/glossary: unfamiliar words		0 1
18.	Cause and effect	L	0 1	43.	Context clues: multiple-meaning words		0 1
19.	Draw conclusions	I	0 1	44.	Context clues: synonyms		0 1
20.	Draw conclusions	C	0 1	45.	Context clues: unfamiliar words		0 1
21.	Cause and effect	I	0 1	46.	Dictionary/glossary: unfamiliar words		0 1
22.	Author's purpose	C	0 1	47.	Context clues: synonyms		0 1
A.	Constructed-response text-to-text connection		0 1 2	48.	Word structure: Greek and Latin roots		0 1
23.	Cause and effect	C	0 1	**Reading – Part 3: Writing Conventions**			
24.	Draw conclusions	I	0 1	49.	Articles		0 1
25.	Draw conclusions	I	0 1	50.	Adverbs		0 1
26.	Fact and opinion	C	0 1	51.	Adjectives		0 1

Reading – Part 3: Writing Conventions (continued)

52.	Pronouns	0 1	57.	Subject/verb agreement	0 1
53.	Dependent clauses	0 1	58.	Using *who* and *whom*	0 1
54.	Irregular verbs	0 1	59	Proper nouns	0 1
55.	Quotation marks	0 1	60.	Irregular plural nouns	0 1
56.	Commas	0 1			

Student's Reading Total Score/Total Possible Score _____ /64

*L = literal   I = inferential   C = critical analysis

Reading — Parts 1–3 percentage score: _____ ÷ 64 = _____ × 100 = _____%

(student's total score)   (percentage score)

Writing – Part 4

Writing Score (complete one)   _____/6   _____/5   _____/4   _____/3

Notes/Observations:

CLASS RECORD CHART
Grade 5 Unit Benchmark Tests

Teacher Name _____   Class _____

Student Name	Unit 1		Unit 2		Unit 3		Unit 4		Unit 5		Unit 6	
	Pt 1–3	Pt 4	Pt 1–3	Pt 4	Pt 1–3	Pt 4	Pt 1–3	Pt 4	Pt 1–3	Pt 4	Pt 1–3	Pt 4
1.												
2.												
3.												
4.												
5.												
6.												
7.												
8.												
9.												
10.												
11.												
12.												
13.												
14.												
15.												
16.												
17.												
18.												
19.												
20.												
21.												
22.												
23.												
24.												
25.												
26.												
27.												
28.												
29.												
30.												

- - - CLASS RECORD CHART -

ANSWER KEYS

Unit 1 Benchmark Test

Reading – Part 1: Comprehension

Selection 1: "Ichiro's Tenth Birthday Party"

1. C
2. J
3. B
4. J
5. A
6. G
7. C
8. F
9. D
10. G
11. A

A. Use the Constructed-Response Scoring Rubric on page T11 to help you assess students' responses. Assign each response a score from 0 to 2.

A possible top response might be:

When Ichiro's birthday plans did not work out, he adapted by changing his plans. When his mother's birthday plans did not work out, she did not change her plans. She adapted by having her brothers instead of her friends as guests.

Selection 2: "The Story of Daedalus: A Retelling of the Greek Myth"

12. G
13. A
14. J
15. A
16. F
17. A
18. H
19. C
20. H
21. D
22. H

B. Use the Constructed-Response Scoring Rubric on page T11 to help you assess students' responses. Assign each response a score from 0 to 2.

A possible top response might be:

Ichiro and Daedalus were alike in that they both had to solve a problem that affected them personally. Ichiro had to figure out how to "escape" the weather, and Daedalus had to figure out how to escape the Labyrinth.

Reading – Part 2: Vocabulary

23. D
24. G
25. B
26. J
27. A
28. F
29. C
30. J
31. A
32. H

Reading – Part 3: Writing Conventions

33. A
34. H
35. C
36. F
37. D

----

38. H

39. B

40. H

Writing – Part 4

Prompt: Students are asked to write a story about when they built something.

Scoring: Use one of the Narrative Writing Scoring Rubrics on pages T12–T13 to help you assess students' compositions. Choose one of the four rubrics, and assign each composition a score based on the 6-point, 5-point, 4-point, or 3-point scale.

Unit 2 Benchmark Test

Reading – Part 1: Comprehension

Selection 1: "The Great Chess Match: Kasparov Versus Deep Blue"

1. B

2. J

3. C

4. J

5. C

6. F

7. C

8. F

9. B

10. G

11. A

A. Use the Constructed-Response Scoring Rubric on page T11 to help you assess students' responses. Assign each response a score from 0 to 2.

A possible top response might be:

Last week, I played in a tennis match against Nancy Lee, the best player on our team. I won the game by hitting a lot of ace serves.

Selection 2: "A Tale of Two Robots"

12. G

13. C

14. H

15. B

16. H

17. B

18. F

19. D

20. F

21. A

22. H

B. Use the Constructed-Response Scoring Rubric on page T11 to help you assess students' responses. Assign each response a score from 0 to 2.

A possible top response might be:

Deep Blue, Doctor R, and Rocky all worked hard to win in competitions. Deep Blue used "thinking" strategies like a human. Doctor R gave Rocky a bandage as a human doctor would. Rocky sang and bowed like a human performer before an audience.

Reading – Part 2: Vocabulary

23. B

24. H

25. D

26. G

27. C

28. J

29. B

30. F

31. A

32. J

Reading – Part 3: Writing Conventions

33. B
34. J
35. B
36. G
37. C
38. H
39. C
40. F

Writing – Part 4

Prompt: Students are asked to write an explanation of a machine and how to operate it. They are to include step-by-step instructions.

Scoring: Use one of the Expository Writing Scoring Rubrics on pages T16–T17 to help you assess students' compositions. Choose one of the four rubrics, and assign each composition a score based on the 6-point, 5-point, 4-point, or 3-point scale.

Unit 3 Benchmark Test

Reading – Part 1: Comprehension

Selection 1: "Naomi Shihab Nye"

1. B
2. H
3. B
4. G
5. A
6. G
7. D
8. J
9. C
10. G
11. A

A. Use the Constructed-Response Scoring Rubric on page T11 to help you assess students' responses. Assign each response a score from 0 to 2.

A possible top response might be:

Reading and writing can change people because when people read and write, they come to know and understand themselves and the world better. If people read a poem by a person from a different country, it might change their ideas or feelings about that place or its people.

Selection 2: "Please Touch"

12. J
13. C
14. H
15. A
16. H
17. B
18. J
19. C
20. G
21. D
22. G

B. Use the Constructed-Response Scoring Rubric on page T11 to help you assess students' responses. Assign each response a score from 0 to 2.

A possible top response might be:

In the first selection, readers learn about people from different places and their feelings by reading poetry and books by Naomi Shihab Nye. In the second selection, Michael Naranjo and visitors to his art shows learn different things about his sculptures by touching them than they would if they only experienced them through sight.

Reading – Part 2: Vocabulary

23. A
24. G
25. D
26. J
27. A
28. F
29. A
30. H
31. B
32. H

Reading – Part 3: Writing Conventions

33. C
34. G
35. D
36. F
37. D
38. G
39. A
40. H

Writing – Part 4

Prompt: Students are asked to select two works of an author and/or an artist and compare the ways the works have affected them.

Scoring: Use one of the Expository Writing Scoring Rubrics on pages T16–T17 to help you assess students' compositions. Choose one of the four rubrics, and assign each composition a score based on the 6-point, 5-point, 4-point, or 3-point scale.

Unit 4 Benchmark Test

Reading – Part 1: Comprehension

Selection 1: "Adapting in Australia"

1. D
2. H
3. D
4. F
5. D
6. F
7. C
8. G
9. D
10. G
11. B

A. Use the Constructed-Response Scoring Rubric on page T11 to help you assess students' responses. Assign each response a score from 0 to 2.

A possible top response might be:

I know this generalization is valid because the selection says the boys were excited about visiting Australia. They learned some facts before coming, such as the information about the box jellyfish. They were willing to try new kinds of food. I also know they were curious because they hurried toward the strange music they heard, and they planned to take a tour of a national park.

Selection 2: "Take a Bite of This"

12. H

13. B

14. J

15. B

16. F

17. A

18. J

19. C

20. F

21. D

22. F

B. Use the Constructed-Response Scoring Rubric on page T11 to help you assess students' responses. Assign each response a score from 0 to 2.

A possible top response might be:

In "Adapting in Australia" the two boys adapt to different foods, music, recreation, and wildlife. "Take a Bite of This" is about the ways in which animals' teeth have adapted to help them survive.

Reading – Part 2: Vocabulary

23. D

24. F

25. D

26. F

27. A

28. H

29. A

30. F

31. B

32. J

Reading – Part 3: Writing Conventions

33. D

34. H

35. A

36. H

37. D

38. H

39. D

40. G

Writing – Part 4

Prompt: Students are asked to write a story about themselves or someone they know who needed to change. The story should include what change was needed and what happened.

Scoring: Use one of the Narrative Writing Scoring Rubrics on pages T12–T13 to help you assess students' compositions. Choose one of the four rubrics, and assign each composition a score based on the 6-point, 5-point, 4-point, or 3-point scale.

Unit 5 Benchmark Test

Reading – Part 1: Comprehension

Selection 1: "Cross Country by Car"

1. A

2. G

3. C

4. J

5. C

6. J

7. A

8. G

9. D

10. G

11. A

A. Use the Constructed-Response Scoring Rubric on page T11 to help you assess students' responses. Assign each response a score from 0 to 2.

A possible top response might be:

Driving conditions today are different because there are paved roads everywhere. There are also gas stations and garages for cars that need fuel or parts. It is much easier to drive cross country now.

Selection 2: "Making Dreams Come True"

12. G

13. A

14. F

15. D

16. H

17. A

18. J

19. C

20. F

21. C

22. J

B. Use the Constructed-Response Scoring Rubric on page T11 to help you assess students' responses. Assign each response a score from 0 to 2.

A possible top response might be:

Jackson and Crocker were like Bancroft and Arnesen because they were adventurous. Both teams set difficult goals and achieved them, so they were all tough and focused.

Reading – Part 2: Vocabulary

23. A

24. G

25. A

26. H

27. C

28. F

29. A

30. H

31. C

32. J

Reading – Part 3: Writing Conventions

33. B

34. J

35. A

36. H

37. A

38. J

39. B

40. G

Writing – Part 4

Prompt: Students are asked to write a persuasive essay to convince classmates to participate in an adventure with them.

Scoring: Use one of the Persuasive Writing Scoring Rubrics on pages T18–T19 to help you assess students' compositions. Choose one of the four rubrics, and assign each composition a score based on the 6-point, 5-point, 4-point, or 3-point scale.

Reading – Part 1: Comprehension

Selection 1: "Dreaming of a Better World"

1. B
2. H
3. A
4. J
5. D
6. G
7. C
8. J
9. A
10. F
11. C

A. Use the Constructed-Response Scoring Rubric on page T11 to help you assess students' responses. Assign each response a score from 0 to 2.

A possible top response might be:

Dean Kamen's inventions are things that help others stay healthy or have more freedom. One example is his robotic wheelchair. It gives users more freedom, and it also allows them to look other people in the eye, which can help them feel more comfortable. Another example is his work on a machine that will purify water for the many people around the world who do not have access to clean water.

Selection 2: "A Creative Mind"

12. G
13. C
14. H
15. B
16. G
17. A
18. H
19. B
20. F
21. D
22. G

B. Use the Constructed-Response Scoring Rubric on page T11 to help you assess students' responses. Assign each response a score from 0 to 2.

A possible top response might be:

Dean Kamen and Sydney are alike because they both have an interest in and the ability to solve problems. Kamen solves problems for others. Sydney solves her own problems.

Reading – Part 2: Vocabulary

23. D
24. F
25. B
26. G
27. A
28. J
29. B
30. J
31. D
32. H

Reading – Part 3: Writing Conventions

33. C
34. J
35. B
36. F
37. B
38. J
39. A
40. H

Writing – Part 4

Prompt: Students are asked to write about a problem and what was done to solve the problem.

Scoring: Use one of the Narrative Writing Scoring Rubrics on pages T12–T13 to help you assess students' compositions. Choose one of the four rubrics, and assign each composition a score based on the 6-point, 5-point, 4-point, or 3-point scale.

End-of-Year Benchmark Test

Reading – Part 1: Comprehension

Selection 1: "Working for the Future"

1. B
2. F
3. D
4. J
5. C
6. F
7. B
8. H

9. C
10. H
11. A

Selection 2: "A Trip Back in Time"

12. G
13. C
14. H
15. D
16. G
17. A
18. J
19. A
20. H
21. D
22. H

A. Use the Constructed-Response Scoring Rubric on page T11 to help you assess students' responses. Assign each response a score from 0 to 2.

A possible top response might be:

Craig and Winsie both cared about the feelings of others. Craig cared about the problems of children he had heard about in other countries. Winsie cared about her mother's feelings. One way they were different was that Craig was trying to help people all over the world and Winsie was trying to help just her own family.

Selection 3: "What's New on the Internet?"

23. C
24. G
25. C
26. J

27. A

28. J

29. D

30. H

31. A

32. G

33. D

B. Use the Constructed-Response Scoring Rubric on page T11 to help you assess students' responses. Assign each response a score from 0 to 2.

A possible top response might be:

Leaving characters on a wall and creating a blog are both ways to communicate with other people. People need computers to create blogs, but not to write on a wall. Blogs can be seen by people who are far away, but the wall has to be seen by people up close. Blogs can be changed or added to, but the wall stays the same.

Reading – Part 2: Vocabulary

34. F

35. C

36. H

37. A

38. G

39. B

40. F

41. C

42. J

43. A

44. F

45. B

46. J

47. D

48. F

Reading – Part 3: Writing Conventions

49. A

50. H

51. D

52. F

53. B

54. H

55. C

56. G

57. D

58. G

59. A

60. J

Writing – Part 4

Prompt: Students are asked to make a convincing argument to persuade readers to support a cause about which they feel strongly.

Scoring: Use one of the Persuasive Writing Scoring Rubrics on pages T18-T19 to help you assess students' compositions. Choose one of the four rubrics, and assign each composition a score based on the 6-point, 5-point, 4-point, or 3-point scale.

ANSWER SHEET
Unit Benchmark Tests

Student Name _____ Unit _____

Teacher Name _____ Date _____

Important Directions for Marking Answers

- Use black lead pencil (No. 2).
- Make heavy dark marks that fill the circle completely.
- Erase completely any answers you wish to change.
- If you erase a grid circle, do not redraw it.
- Do not make any stray marks on this answer sheet.

CORRECT MARK

Ⓐ ● Ⓒ Ⓓ

INCORRECT MARKS

Reading – Part 1: Comprehension

1. Ⓐ Ⓑ Ⓒ Ⓓ	6. Ⓕ Ⓖ Ⓗ Ⓙ	11. Ⓐ Ⓑ Ⓒ Ⓓ	16. Ⓕ Ⓖ Ⓗ Ⓙ	21. Ⓐ Ⓑ Ⓒ Ⓓ
2. Ⓕ Ⓖ Ⓗ Ⓙ	7. Ⓐ Ⓑ Ⓒ Ⓓ	12. Ⓕ Ⓖ Ⓗ Ⓙ	17. Ⓐ Ⓑ Ⓒ Ⓓ	22. Ⓕ Ⓖ Ⓗ Ⓙ
3. Ⓐ Ⓑ Ⓒ Ⓓ	8. Ⓕ Ⓖ Ⓗ Ⓙ	13. Ⓐ Ⓑ Ⓒ Ⓓ	18. Ⓕ Ⓖ Ⓗ Ⓙ	
4. Ⓕ Ⓖ Ⓗ Ⓙ	9. Ⓐ Ⓑ Ⓒ Ⓓ	14. Ⓕ Ⓖ Ⓗ Ⓙ	19. Ⓐ Ⓑ Ⓒ Ⓓ	
5. Ⓐ Ⓑ Ⓒ Ⓓ	10. Ⓕ Ⓖ Ⓗ Ⓙ	15. Ⓐ Ⓑ Ⓒ Ⓓ	20. Ⓕ Ⓖ Ⓗ Ⓙ	

Reading – Part 2: Vocabulary

23. Ⓐ Ⓑ Ⓒ Ⓓ	25. Ⓐ Ⓑ Ⓒ Ⓓ	27. Ⓐ Ⓑ Ⓒ Ⓓ	29. Ⓐ Ⓑ Ⓒ Ⓓ	31. Ⓐ Ⓑ Ⓒ Ⓓ
24. Ⓕ Ⓖ Ⓗ Ⓙ	26. Ⓕ Ⓖ Ⓗ Ⓙ	28. Ⓕ Ⓖ Ⓗ Ⓙ	30. Ⓕ Ⓖ Ⓗ Ⓙ	32. Ⓕ Ⓖ Ⓗ Ⓙ

Reading – Part 3: Writing Conventions

33. Ⓐ Ⓑ Ⓒ Ⓓ	35. Ⓐ Ⓑ Ⓒ Ⓓ	37. Ⓐ Ⓑ Ⓒ Ⓓ	39. Ⓐ Ⓑ Ⓒ Ⓓ
34. Ⓕ Ⓖ Ⓗ Ⓙ	36. Ⓕ Ⓖ Ⓗ Ⓙ	38. Ⓕ Ⓖ Ⓗ Ⓙ	40. Ⓕ Ⓖ Ⓗ Ⓙ

■ ■

ANSWER SHEET
End-of-Year Benchmark Test

Student Name _____ Date _____

Teacher Name _____

Important Directions for Marking Answers

- Use black lead pencil (No. 2).
- Make heavy dark marks that fill the circle completely.
- Erase completely any answers you wish to change.
- If you erase a grid circle, do not redraw it.
- Do not make any stray marks on this answer sheet.

CORRECT MARK

Ⓐ ● Ⓒ Ⓓ

INCORRECT MARKS

Reading – Part 1: Comprehension

1. Ⓐ Ⓑ Ⓒ Ⓓ	8. Ⓕ Ⓖ Ⓗ Ⓙ	15. Ⓐ Ⓑ Ⓒ Ⓓ	22. Ⓕ Ⓖ Ⓗ Ⓙ	29. Ⓐ Ⓑ Ⓒ Ⓓ
2. Ⓕ Ⓖ Ⓗ Ⓙ	9. Ⓐ Ⓑ Ⓒ Ⓓ	16. Ⓕ Ⓖ Ⓗ Ⓙ	23. Ⓐ Ⓑ Ⓒ Ⓓ	30. Ⓕ Ⓖ Ⓗ Ⓙ
3. Ⓐ Ⓑ Ⓒ Ⓓ	10. Ⓕ Ⓖ Ⓗ Ⓙ	17. Ⓐ Ⓑ Ⓒ Ⓓ	24. Ⓕ Ⓖ Ⓗ Ⓙ	31. Ⓐ Ⓑ Ⓒ Ⓓ
4. Ⓕ Ⓖ Ⓗ Ⓙ	11. Ⓐ Ⓑ Ⓒ Ⓓ	18. Ⓕ Ⓖ Ⓗ Ⓙ	25. Ⓐ Ⓑ Ⓒ Ⓓ	32. Ⓕ Ⓖ Ⓗ Ⓙ
5. Ⓐ Ⓑ Ⓒ Ⓓ	12. Ⓕ Ⓖ Ⓗ Ⓙ	19. Ⓐ Ⓑ Ⓒ Ⓓ	26. Ⓕ Ⓖ Ⓗ Ⓙ	33. Ⓐ Ⓑ Ⓒ Ⓓ
6. Ⓕ Ⓖ Ⓗ Ⓙ	13. Ⓐ Ⓑ Ⓒ Ⓓ	20. Ⓕ Ⓖ Ⓗ Ⓙ	27. Ⓐ Ⓑ Ⓒ Ⓓ	
7. Ⓐ Ⓑ Ⓒ Ⓓ	14. Ⓕ Ⓖ Ⓗ Ⓙ	21. Ⓐ Ⓑ Ⓒ Ⓓ	28. Ⓕ Ⓖ Ⓗ Ⓙ	

Reading – Part 2: Vocabulary

34. Ⓕ Ⓖ Ⓗ Ⓙ	37. Ⓐ Ⓑ Ⓒ Ⓓ	40. Ⓕ Ⓖ Ⓗ Ⓙ	43. Ⓐ Ⓑ Ⓒ Ⓓ	46. Ⓕ Ⓖ Ⓗ Ⓙ
35. Ⓐ Ⓑ Ⓒ Ⓓ	38. Ⓕ Ⓖ Ⓗ Ⓙ	41. Ⓐ Ⓑ Ⓒ Ⓓ	44. Ⓕ Ⓖ Ⓗ Ⓙ	47. Ⓐ Ⓑ Ⓒ Ⓓ
36. Ⓕ Ⓖ Ⓗ Ⓙ	39. Ⓐ Ⓑ Ⓒ Ⓓ	42. Ⓕ Ⓖ Ⓗ Ⓙ	45. Ⓐ Ⓑ Ⓒ Ⓓ	48. Ⓕ Ⓖ Ⓗ Ⓙ

Reading – Part 3: Writing Conventions

49. Ⓐ Ⓑ Ⓒ Ⓓ	52. Ⓕ Ⓖ Ⓗ Ⓙ	55. Ⓐ Ⓑ Ⓒ Ⓓ	58. Ⓕ Ⓖ Ⓗ Ⓙ
50. Ⓕ Ⓖ Ⓗ Ⓙ	53. Ⓐ Ⓑ Ⓒ Ⓓ	56. Ⓕ Ⓖ Ⓗ Ⓙ	59. Ⓐ Ⓑ Ⓒ Ⓓ
51. Ⓐ Ⓑ Ⓒ Ⓓ	54. Ⓕ Ⓖ Ⓗ Ⓙ	57. Ⓐ Ⓑ Ⓒ Ⓓ	60. Ⓕ Ⓖ Ⓗ Ⓙ

OPTIONAL — FLUENCY CHECKS OR RUNNING RECORDS

How to Administer and Score a Fluency Test

A fluency test measures a student's reading rate, or the number of words correctly read per minute (wcpm), on grade-level text the student has not seen before. Give the student a copy of the Student Copy of the passage for the test and make a copy of the Teacher Copy for yourself, noting the formula for calculation at the bottom of the page. (The Teacher Copy has a scale of running numbers to make it easier for you to know how many words the student read during the fluency check, while the passages in the student edition do not have the numbers.) Make sure you have put the student's name and the test date at the top of your copy of the passage. Have a watch or clock with a second hand available for timing the reading.

Have the student read the text aloud. Do not have the student read the title as part of the fluency reading; it is not included in the running word count. (You may want to tape-record the student's reading for later evaluation.) Stop the student at exactly one minute and note precisely where the student stopped.

As the student reads orally, on your copy of the text, mark any miscues or errors the student makes during the reading (see the chart on page T58). Count the total number of words the student read in one minute. Subtract any words the student read incorrectly. Record the words correct per minute (wcpm) score on the test.

The formula is: Total # of words read – # of errors = words correct per minute (wcpm).

How to Identify Reading Miscues/Errors

Using the passage on page T59, the chart below shows the kinds of miscues and errors to look for as a student reads aloud, and the notations to use to mark them.

Reading Miscue	Notations
Omission The student omits words or word parts.	All of us animals (have) agreed to live peacefully from now on.
Substitution The student substitutes words or parts of words for the words in the text.	As he passed *the* ~~a~~ farm, he heard a rooster crow.
Insertion The student inserts words or parts of words that are not in the text.	Finally, he spied the bird sitting high ∧*up* in a tree.
Mispronunciation/Misreading The student pronounces or reads a word incorrectly.	The fox licked his chops and looked around, hoping to sight *see* the rooster.
Hesitation The student hesitates over a word, and the teacher provides the word.	"Oh, I can't do that," *H* <u>replied</u> the rooster.
Self-correction The student reads a word incorrectly but then corrects the error.	One morning, a hungry fox trotted (SC) along looking for his breakfast.

Notes

- If the student hesitates over a word, wait several seconds before telling the student what the word is.

- If a student makes the same error more than once, count it as only one error.

- Self-correction is not counted as an actual error. However, writing "SC" over the word or words will help you identify words that give the student some difficulty.

Sample Fluency Test

Here is the passage marked as shown on the chart on the previous page. As the student reads the passage aloud to you, mark miscues and errors. Have the student read for exactly one minute, and then mark the last word the student reads.

Student Name _Susan_   Date _9/7/2011_

The Fox and the Rooster   (112)

One morning, a hungry fox trotted (sc) along looking for his breakfast. As he passed	14
a(the) farm, he heard a rooster crow. The fox licked his chops and looked around, hoping	30
to sight(see) the rooster. Finally, he spied the bird sitting high up in a tree.	44
"Good morning, friend!" the fox called out. "Come down and have a friendly	57
chat with me!"	60
"Oh, I can't do that," replied(H) the rooster. "You would eat me for sure."	74
"You haven't heard the news, then," the fox said in a surprised tone. "All of us	90
animals (have) agreed to live peacefully from now on. We aren't allowed to eat one	105
another anymore."	107
The rooster did not answer. Instead, he began to look / into the distance with great	122
interest. He cocked his head as if he heard something, but the fox heard nothing. As a	138
result, the fox became curious.	144
"What's going on?" asked the fox. "What do you see? What do you hear?"	158

_117−5=112_

Interpreting the Results

According to published norms for oral reading fluency, students at the end of Grade 5 should be reading fluently at 140 words correct per minute in text that is on grade level. This chart gives recommended progress toward that goal.

End of Unit/Grade		Reading Rate (wcpm)
Grade 5	Unit 1	105 to 110
Grade 5	Unit 2	110 to 116
Grade 5	Unit 3	115 to 122
Grade 5	Unit 4	120 to 128
Grade 5	Unit 5	125 to 134
Grade 5	Unit 6	130 to 140
End-of-Year Goal		140

If a student's reading rate is lower than the suggested progress toward the standard for his or her grade level, your notes on the student's miscues may help you determine why the rate is low. Does the student make errors that indicate his or her decoding skills are poor? If so, further instruction in phonics may be needed. Do the errors reflect a lack of comprehension or limited vocabulary? In that case, instruction in comprehension strategies and exposure to more vocabulary words may help. A lack of fluency may indicate a lack of exposure to models of fluent oral reading. It may also mean that the student isn't reading enough material at his or her reading level.

How to Take a Running Record

A Running Record is an assessment of oral reading accuracy and oral reading fluency. A student's reading accuracy is based on the number of words read correctly. This measure is determined by an analysis of the errors a student makes—a miscue analysis. Reading fluency is based on reading rate (the number of words read per minute) and the degree to which the student reads with a "natural flow."

A Running Record may be taken using any reading passage at any time. However, the most valid and reliable assessment fulfills these requirements: (1) the text is appropriate to the student's reading level and interest; and (2) the text is unfamiliar to the student. The passages in this section are well-suited for use as either a Fluency Test or a Running Record because they fit these requirements. For additional oral reading accuracy and fluency checks that involve a Running Record, you may choose other passages from grade-level appropriate texts.

The Running Record may be used to verify instructional decisions suggested by other assessments, such as a Placement or Benchmark Test. It may also be used to identify a student's particular strengths and weaknesses in reading and language development. In addition, the Running Record may be administered periodically throughout the year as a means of monitoring student progress.

Measuring oral reading accuracy and oral reading fluency may be accomplished in a single reading, but two different operations are required. The guidelines on pages T62 and T63 explain how to determine each measurement.

How to Measure Oral Reading Accuracy

1. Choose an appropriate grade-level text of about 100 to 200 words, or use those passages that have been provided for use as a Fluency Test.

2. Make copies of the text—one of the Student Copy for the student and one of the Teacher Copy for you. If the text appears in a book, you may have the student read the text from the book.

3. Give the text to the student and have the student read the text aloud. (You may want to tape-record the student's reading for later evaluation. This approach can be especially helpful if you are timing the student's reading or conducting other assessments at the same time.)

4. Your hand should always be "running" on your copy of the text. Put a checkmark above every word the student reads correctly. Mark any miscues or errors the student makes during the reading (see the explanation of reading miscues/errors for Fluency Tests beginning on page T58).

5. Count the total number of errors the student makes and find the percentage score for the number of errors. If you are using a fluency/running record passage from this book, the total word count is indicated for each passage and a formula for determining a percentage score is provided.

6. If you are using a text from a different source, use this formula to get a percentage score:

$$\frac{\text{Total \# of words minus \# of errors}}{\text{Total \# of words}} \times 100 = \text{percentage score}$$

Example: Suppose a student reads a text of 110 words and makes 6 errors.

$$\frac{110 - 6 = 104 \text{ words}}{110} = 0.945 \qquad 0.945 \times 100 = 94.5\% \text{ (round to 95\%)}$$

The percentage score indicates the student's oral reading accuracy (percentage of words in the passage read correctly).

How to Measure Reading Rate

Reading rate is generally defined as number of words read per minute (wpm). To determine the reading rate, follow steps 1–3 as described on page T62. Note the exact time when the student begins reading and the time when he or she finishes.

To calculate the number of words per minute, use the formula below:

$$\frac{\text{Total \# of words read}}{\text{\# of seconds}} \times 60 = \text{words per minute}$$

Example: Suppose a student reads a passage of 120 words in 90 seconds.

$$\frac{120}{90} = 1.33 \text{ (round to the nearest hundredth)}$$

$$1.33 \times 60 = 79.8 \text{ words per minute (round to 80 wpm)}$$

Interpreting the Results

For oral reading accuracy, use the following criteria:

- A student who reads 98%–100% of the words correctly is reading at an independent level and may need more challenging texts.

- A student who reads 91%–97% of the words correctly is reading at an instructional level and will likely benefit from guided on-level instruction in the regular program.

- A student who reads with an accuracy of 90% or less is reading at a frustration level and may benefit most from targeted instruction with lower-level texts or strategic intervention.

For any student whose Running Record results are not clearly definitive, we recommend administering additional individual assessments, such as classroom observations and anecdotal records. For more information about other assessments, refer to the *Assessment Handbook*.

On the following pages you will find passages that may be used for either Fluency or Running Record Tests. Both a Teacher Copy and a Student Copy have been provided.

Student Name _____ Date _____

How I Surprised Myself

I'm a shy person, and I like quiet and order. My whole family is the same way.	17
We all stay at home a lot because we have hobbies we enjoy. For instance, my	33
mother likes to knit—she's always making afghans to give away. My father has a	48
winter hobby, making furniture; and a summer hobby, growing roses.	58
My first hobby was collecting stickers, and my second was making photo	70
albums. Now my mother is teaching me to crochet, and I'm planning to make	84
scarves for my mother, father, sister, and myself.	92
A few weeks ago, my mother approached me about a summer camp. It was	106
for one week, and there would be activities such as horseback riding, crafts, and	120
swimming. At first, I didn't want to go. Where would I sleep? What would the food	136
be like? Would I have fun? My mother said she wouldn't send me if I really didn't	153
want to go. But she had my best friend, Laticia, come over and talk to me, and	170
Laticia persuaded me to go.	175
Now here's the surprising part. I actually had a great time. The best part was	190
that I learned to ride a horse. I made a lot of friends too. All the girls slept in	209
sleeping bags in bunks, and it was like a slumber party. Even the food was OK.	225

Fluency Test

□ − □ = □ (wcpm)

Running Record

Oral Reading Accuracy:

$$\frac{□ − □}{□} \times 100 = □ \%$$

Reading Rate:

$$\frac{□}{□} \times 60 = □ \text{ (wpm)}$$

How I Surprised Myself

I'm a shy person, and I like quiet and order. My whole family is the same way. We all stay at home a lot because we have hobbies we enjoy. For instance, my mother likes to knit—she's always making afghans to give away. My father has a winter hobby, making furniture; and a summer hobby, growing roses.

My first hobby was collecting stickers, and my second was making photo albums. Now my mother is teaching me to crochet, and I'm planning to make scarves for my mother, father, sister, and myself.

A few weeks ago, my mother approached me about a summer camp. It was for one week, and there would be activities such as horseback riding, crafts, and swimming. At first, I didn't want to go. Where would I sleep? What would the food be like? Would I have fun? My mother said she wouldn't send me if I really didn't want to go. But she had my best friend, Laticia, come over and talk to me, and Laticia persuaded me to go.

Now here's the surprising part. I actually had a great time. The best part was that I learned to ride a horse. I made a lot of friends too. All the girls slept in sleeping bags in bunks, and it was like a slumber party. Even the food was OK.

Student Name _____ Date _____

The Yo-yo

"Maria," her mother called. "Get your coat on, please. We're going to the | 13
grocery store." | 15

"But, Mom," Maria asked, "why do I have to go?" | 25

"Maria," her mother replied, "you know I need your help with the twins." The | 39
twins her mother was referring to were Maria's brothers, Brian and Dan, who were | 53
two and a half. | 57

Maria put her coat on, scowled at her brothers, and jammed her hands in her | 72
pockets. Surprised, she retrieved a yo-yo from her left pocket. Her friend Amy | 85
had given it to her a few months ago and had also taught her a complicated, | 101
impressive trick. | 103

One hour later, they had finished shopping and were heading to the checkout. | 116
"Oh, I forgot the cauliflower," Maria's mother said. "You stay here and watch the | 130
boys while I go get it." Maria nodded. Several minutes passed. Brian was squirming | 144
and trying to climb out of the cart, and Dan began to get fussy. | 158

Maria sighed. "Where is Mom?" she wondered. Then she remembered her | 169
yo-yo. "Hey, Brian, Dan," she said. "Watch this." She showed them her yo-yo trick. | 183
The boys' eyes followed as the yo-yo swung up and down. Dan stopped fussing, | 197
and Brian smiled and bounced in his seat. | 205

Maria's mother returned, and, watching Maria with the boys, she said, "Maria, | 217
remember when you asked about taking a baby-sitting course? I think that's an | 230
excellent idea." | 232

Fluency Test

[ ] − [ ] = [ ] (wcpm)

Running Record

Oral Reading Accuracy: Reading Rate:

$$\frac{[\ ] - [\ ]}{[\ ]} \times 100 = [\quad] \%$$

$$\frac{[\ ]}{[\ ]} \times 60 = [\qquad] \text{ (wpm)}$$

- -

The Yo-yo

"Maria," her mother called. "Get your coat on, please. We're going to the grocery store."

"But, Mom," Maria asked, "why do I have to go?"

"Maria," her mother replied, "you know I need your help with the twins." The twins her mother was referring to were Maria's brothers, Brian and Dan, who were two and a half.

Maria put her coat on, scowled at her brothers, and jammed her hands in her pockets. Surprised, she retrieved a yo-yo from her left pocket. Her friend Amy had given it to her a few months ago and had also taught her a complicated, impressive trick.

One hour later, they had finished shopping and were heading to the checkout. "Oh, I forgot the cauliflower," Maria's mother said. "You stay here and watch the boys while I go get it." Maria nodded. Several minutes passed. Brian was squirming and trying to climb out of the cart, and Dan began to get fussy.

Maria sighed. "Where is Mom?" she wondered. Then she remembered her yo-yo. "Hey, Brian, Dan," she said. "Watch this." She showed them her yo-yo trick. The boys' eyes followed as the yo-yo swung up and down. Dan stopped fussing, and Brian smiled and bounced in his seat.

Maria's mother returned, and, watching Maria with the boys, she said, "Maria, remember when you asked about taking a baby-sitting course? I think that's an excellent idea."

Student Name _____ Date _____

Your Feet

Do you ever think about your feet—I mean, really think about them? Probably	14
not … not unless they're hurting. If your shoes are uncomfortable, you probably	26
yank them off and moan, "My feet are killing me!" If you get a cut or abrasion on	44
one of your feet, you may give it special care for a while, keeping the wound clean	61
and putting on antibiotic ointment; but when the wound heals, you forget about	74
your feet again.	77
Well, it's time to change your attitude toward your feet. You need to give	91
them some attention, just as you give attention to your face and your hair. In your	107
lifetime, each of your feet is going to hit the ground, floor, and stairs nearly ten	123
million times. The entire weight of your body comes down on your feet with each	138
step—that's a lot of wear and tear!	146
The most important thing you can do for your feet is to get yourself some	161
good shoes. Not shoes that look good but shoes that feel good—shoes that don't	176
compress the toes all together, shoes that are large enough to prevent calluses or	190
bunions, shoes that are comfortable. Exercise is also crucial for the health of your	204
feet, and the best exercise for your feet is walking.	214
So, don't "look down on" your feet anymore. Give them the respect they	227
deserve. And the next time you buy shoes, think less about fashion and more	241
about comfort.	243

Fluency Test

☐ − ☐ = ☐ (wcpm)

Running Record

Oral Reading Accuracy:

$$\frac{\boxed{} - \boxed{}}{\boxed{}} \times 100 = \boxed{} \%$$

Reading Rate:

$$\frac{\boxed{}}{\boxed{}} \times 60 = \boxed{} \text{ (wpm)}$$

Your Feet

Do you ever think about your feet—I mean, really think about them? Probably not … not unless they're hurting. If your shoes are uncomfortable, you probably yank them off and moan, "My feet are killing me!" If you get a cut or abrasion on one of your feet, you may give it special care for a while, keeping the wound clean and putting on antibiotic ointment; but when the wound heals, you forget about your feet again.

Well, it's time to change your attitude toward your feet. You need to give them some attention, just as you give attention to your face and your hair. In your lifetime, each of your feet is going to hit the ground, floor, and stairs nearly ten million times. The entire weight of your body comes down on your feet with each step—that's a lot of wear and tear!

The most important thing you can do for your feet is to get yourself some good shoes. Not shoes that look good but shoes that feel good—shoes that don't compress the toes all together, shoes that are large enough to prevent calluses or bunions, shoes that are comfortable. Exercise is also crucial for the health of your feet, and the best exercise for your feet is walking.

So, don't "look down on" your feet anymore. Give them the respect they deserve. And the next time you buy shoes, think less about fashion and more about comfort.

Student Name _____ Date _____

Moving On

As Josh's mother came into the kitchen, she saw Josh sitting at the table playing | 15

with a pencil and staring gloomily out the window. "Hi, honey," Josh's mom said. | 29

"Hi, Mom," Josh said. His voice was flat. | 37

His mother looked at him. "What's wrong, Josh?" she asked. | 47

"Max is moving to Ohio," Josh said in a trembling voice. Max was Josh's best friend. | 63

"Oh no, I'm so sorry to hear that," said Josh's mom sympathetically. Since | 76

kindergarten, Max and Josh had been inseparable. They went to school together, | 88

played on the same soccer team, and even celebrated their birthdays together. | 100

"Maybe Max can come visit in the summer," his mother said. "Ohio's not that | 114

far away." | 116

"Yeah, maybe," Josh said quietly. He looked utterly dejected. | 125

Josh's eighteen-year-old brother hurried into the kitchen. Donovan had just | 135

graduated from high school. "I'm going to Vince's, Mom," he said. "I want to see | 150

him before he leaves. It'll be several months before I see him again." | 163

"Where's he going?" Josh asked. | 168

"He's going away to college," Donovan said. "He's leaving this weekend. You | 180

knew that." Josh did know, but he had forgotten. | 189

"OK, honey," Mom said as Donovan banged out the back door. "Don't be too | 203

late. And drive carefully!" She sighed as she turned from the door. | 215

Wow, Josh thought. Donovan's best friend is leaving town too, but he's not moping | 229

around. He's already looking forward to when they'll get together again. Maybe Max | 242

could come visit in the summer—after all, Ohio was only two states away. | 256

Fluency Test

	−		=		(wcpm)

Running Record

Oral Reading Accuracy: Reading Rate:

$$\frac{\boxed{} - \boxed{}}{\boxed{}} \times 100 = \boxed{} \% \qquad \frac{\boxed{}}{\boxed{}} \times 60 = \boxed{} \text{ (wpm)}$$

- -

Moving On

As Josh's mother came into the kitchen, she saw Josh sitting at the table playing with a pencil and staring gloomily out the window. "Hi, honey," Josh's mom said.

"Hi, Mom," Josh said. His voice was flat.

His mother looked at him. "What's wrong, Josh?" she asked.

"Max is moving to Ohio," Josh said in a trembling voice. Max was Josh's best friend.

"Oh no, I'm so sorry to hear that," said Josh's mom sympathetically. Since kindergarten, Max and Josh had been inseparable. They went to school together, played on the same soccer team, and even celebrated their birthdays together.

"Maybe Max can come visit in the summer," his mother said. "Ohio's not that far away."

"Yeah, maybe," Josh said quietly. He looked utterly dejected.

Josh's eighteen-year-old brother hurried into the kitchen. Donovan had just graduated from high school. "I'm going to Vince's, Mom," he said. "I want to see him before he leaves. It'll be several months before I see him again."

"Where's he going?" Josh asked.

"He's going away to college," Donovan said. "He's leaving this weekend. You knew that." Josh did know, but he had forgotten.

"OK, honey," Mom said as Donovan banged out the back door. "Don't be too late. And drive carefully!" She sighed as she turned from the door.

Wow, Josh thought. Donovan's best friend is leaving town too, but he's not moping around. He's already looking forward to when they'll get together again. Maybe Max *could* come visit in the summer—after all, Ohio was only two states away.

Student Name _____ Date _____

Adobe Houses

When the Spanish explorers came to the area that is now known as New	14
Mexico, they found Native Americans living in small villages. Their houses were	26
made from mud, sand, grass, and water that were mixed together, formed into	39
blocks, and then dried in the sun. The Spanish called this material adobe.	52
Adobe houses are very practical in a place like New Mexico that has very few	67
trees and plenty of hard earth, and adobe is still used often in the Southwest. It	83
is inexpensive to use because the materials used to make adobe are plentiful and	97
cheap.	98
The way adobe is made has not changed much over the years. The materials are	113
mixed to form a mud, which is placed in forms shaped like bricks that are then left	130
in the sun to dry. Later, the bricks are removed from the forms and left to dry some	148
more, about two weeks in all, until they are ready to be stored or used.	163
Adobe houses of today are more durable than ever because new methods have	176
been developed for keeping the adobe dry. Concrete is placed under the walls to	190
keep them elevated off the ground. A hard covering called stucco is put on both the	206
insides and outsides of the walls to protect them. The roof is sloped so rain will run	223
off and not get inside the house.	230
Adobe saves money after the house is built too. The walls are so thick—ten	245
to twelve inches—that the house stays warm during the winter and cool in the	260
summer, cutting down on heating and air-conditioning bills.	268

Fluency Test

[ ] − [ ] = [ ] (wcpm)

Running Record

Oral Reading Accuracy: Reading Rate:

$$\frac{[\quad] - [\quad]}{[\quad]} \times 100 = [\quad\quad]\%$$

$$\frac{[\quad]}{[\quad]} \times 60 = [\quad\quad] \text{ (wpm)}$$

Adobe Houses

When the Spanish explorers came to the area that is now known as New Mexico, they found Native Americans living in small villages. Their houses were made from mud, sand, grass, and water that were mixed together, formed into blocks, and then dried in the sun. The Spanish called this material adobe.

Adobe houses are very practical in a place like New Mexico that has very few trees and plenty of hard earth, and adobe is still used often in the Southwest. It is inexpensive to use because the materials used to make adobe are plentiful and cheap.

The way adobe is made has not changed much over the years. The materials are mixed to form a mud, which is placed in forms shaped like bricks that are then left in the sun to dry. Later, the bricks are removed from the forms and left to dry some more, about two weeks in all, until they are ready to be stored or used.

Adobe houses of today are more durable than ever because new methods have been developed for keeping the adobe dry. Concrete is placed under the walls to keep them elevated off the ground. A hard covering called stucco is put on both the insides and outsides of the walls to protect them. The roof is sloped so rain will run off and not get inside the house.

Adobe saves money after the house is built too. The walls are so thick—ten to twelve inches—that the house stays warm during the winter and cool in the summer, cutting down on heating and air-conditioning bills.

Student Name _____ Date _____

The Cork Tree

Most trees would die if you stripped off their bark. However, there is a kind	15
of tree that people have been removing the bark from for hundreds of years.	29
Amazingly, this tree regenerates its bark and continues to live and thrive. This tree	43
is the cork tree, a species of oak that grows mostly along the Mediterranean Sea.	58

You probably know about cork from having seen bulletin boards made of it. | 71
Many schools and other public buildings have cork flooring, and a popular kind | 84
of running track is made of cork. For centuries, cork has been used in the soles of | 101
shoes and sandals. | 104

In addition, cork has many uses that you don't see. Because of its buoyancy, it | 119
is used in life jackets. Cork is a thermal insulator used to keep food hot, cold, or | 136
frozen, so it is commonly used in food-storage buildings and in trucks and | 149
railroad cars that transport food. | 154

Cork is the outermost dead layer of bark on the tree; it can be removed without | 170
injuring the tree. Beneath the cork is the living layer of bark, and its preservation | 185
is essential for the tree's survival. The tree is about twenty years old when the first | 201
cork-harvesting operation takes place. Workers cut the cork from the trunk and from | 214
the large branches in four- to ten-foot-long sheets. Extreme care is taken to avoid | 228
damaging the living bark. | 232

The tree recovers from the removal of the cork in three months, but it will take | 248
about ten years to grow a new layer and for the outermost layer to die and be ready | 266
for the next harvest. With good care a cork tree will live 150 years or more. | 282

Fluency Test

[   ] – [   ] = [   ] (wcpm)

Running Record

Oral Reading Accuracy:

$$\frac{[\quad] - [\quad]}{[\quad]} \times 100 = \boxed{\quad\%}$$

Reading Rate:

$$\frac{[\quad]}{[\quad]} \times 60 = \boxed{\quad} \text{(wpm)}$$

The Cork Tree

Most trees would die if you stripped off their bark. However, there is a kind of tree that people have been removing the bark from for hundreds of years. Amazingly, this tree regenerates its bark and continues to live and thrive. This tree is the cork tree, a species of oak that grows mostly along the Mediterranean Sea.

You probably know about cork from having seen bulletin boards made of it. Many schools and other public buildings have cork flooring, and a popular kind of running track is made of cork. For centuries, cork has been used in the soles of shoes and sandals.

In addition, cork has many uses that you don't see. Because of its buoyancy, it is used in life jackets. Cork is a thermal insulator used to keep food hot, cold, or frozen, so it is commonly used in food-storage buildings and in trucks and railroad cars that transport food.

Cork is the outermost dead layer of bark on the tree; it can be removed without injuring the tree. Beneath the cork is the living layer of bark, and its preservation is essential for the tree's survival. The tree is about twenty years old when the first cork-harvesting operation takes place. Workers cut the cork from the trunk and from the large branches in four- to ten-foot-long sheets. Extreme care is taken to avoid damaging the living bark.

The tree recovers from the removal of the cork in three months, but it will take about ten years to grow a new layer and for the outermost layer to die and be ready for the next harvest. With good care a cork tree will live 150 years or more.

NAME _____ DATE _____

Scott Foresman
Benchmark Test
Unit 1
Meeting Challenges

Glenview, Illinois
Boston, Massachusetts
Chandler, Arizona
Upper Saddle River, New Jersey

ISBN-13: 978-0-328-53751-8
ISBN-10:   0-328-53751-9

1 2 3 4 5 6 7 8 9 10 V011 19 18 17 16 15 14 13 12 11 10
CC1

ISBN-13: 978-0-328-53751-8
ISBN-10:   0-328-53751-9

EAN

9 780328 537518

90000>

Directions

When the weather ruins Ichiro's plan for his birthday, he fashions a new plan. Read about the events that happened. Then do Numbers 1 through 11.

Ichiro's Tenth Birthday Party

It was the summer before Ichiro started fifth grade, and he was about to turn ten. His family had just moved to a new city, so he didn't know many other children, but his mother suggested that he host a birthday party and invite some of the friends he had made during the summer. Ichiro sent an invitation to each friend. He was thrilled by the idea of a party. His excitement grew as the day approached.

Ichiro's favorite sport was swimming, so he had sent out the invitations for a pool party at the city activities center, which had not only a small outdoor pool but also a gymnasium with basketball and volleyball courts. On the morning of the party, however, Ichiro became sad; he awoke to discover that it was pouring rain.

"What should I do?" he asked his mother. She saw how disappointed he was by looking at the forlorn expression on his face, so she sat him down, handed him a glass of juice, and said, "Don't worry! Let me tell you a story."

Ichiro's mother had grown up in a small town in Idaho, and she began telling him about the time she tried to have a birthday party for herself when she turned ten. Her best friends, Eliza and Junko, were to come to her house for an elegant tea party her mother had specially prepared. However, the night before her birthday, a blizzard blew in, covering her town with snow and making it impossible for anyone to drive anywhere for days.

"What did you do?" Ichiro asked his mother.

She explained that her mother hosted the tea party for her and her older brothers. "Your uncles," she told him, "actually enjoyed it!" Later in the week, Junko and Eliza came by to celebrate her birthday, and they all built a cave in the snow and drank hot cocoa inside it. "We'll figure out something to do for your party too," she told Ichiro.

Instead of a pool party, they decided on a basketball game; basketball was Ichiro's second favorite sport. His new friends enjoyed themselves, and later he looked back on that birthday as one of his best, even though things did not turn out exactly as planned.

1 **Which of the following words best describes Ichiro's mother?**

A nervous

B lonely

C kind

D athletic

2 **Why was Ichiro sad on the morning of his tenth birthday?**

F He didn't like parties.

G No one could come to his party.

H Birthdays made him feel old.

J His pool party could not be held in the rain.

3 What happened as a result of the blizzard in Ichiro's mother's town in Idaho?

A His mother's brothers built a snow cave in the backyard.

B His mother's friends Eliza and Junko could not come to the tea party.

C His mother decided not to celebrate her birthday.

D His mother's mother suggested rescheduling the tea party.

4 How did Ichiro feel later about his tenth birthday party?

F He was still disappointed.

G He wished he had invited more people.

H He did not remember it.

J He thought it was one of his best parties ever.

5 Which word best describes Ichiro?

A adaptable

B confident

C stubborn

D lazy

6 The author probably wrote this selection to

F explain why it is important to learn how to swim.

G tell an entertaining story about a boy's birthday.

H describe weather patterns in different places.

J give information about growing up in Idaho.

7 Why did Ichiro's mother tell him about her childhood?

A to convince him to make new friends

B to show how nice his uncles were

C to cheer him up about the party

D to explain her friends' actions

8 Which event happened after Ichiro's mother told her story?

F They decided to have a basketball party.

G Ichiro planned a party with swimming.

H Ichiro woke up to a rainy morning.

J Ichiro's mother gave him some juice.

9 In what way are Ichiro and his mother alike?

   A   Both drank hot cocoa inside a snow cave.

   B   Both spent their tenth birthdays with their best friends.

   C   Both preferred swimming to basketball.

   D   Both went along with changes in plans.

10 Which of the following occurred last in the story?

   F   Ichiro made friends in a new city during the summer.

   G   Ichiro looked back fondly on his tenth birthday party.

   H   Ichiro mailed out invitations to his pool party.

   J   Junko and Eliza came to Ichiro's mother's house.

11 Which of the following is the most important theme of the story?

   A   Some of the best memories are of challenging situations.

   B   Disappointment feels worse on your birthday.

   C   It's important to tell people how you feel at all times.

   D   Few friends can be counted on in bad weather.

GO ON

Directions

Write your answer to Question A on the lines below. Base your answer on "Ichiro's Tenth Birthday Party."

A What was the main difference between Ichiro's tenth birthday and his mother's tenth birthday? Use details from the selection to explain your answer.

_____

_____

_____

_____

_____

_____

_____

_____

_____

Directions

The architect Daedalus could not have anticipated ending up trapped in one of his own designs. Read how he escaped. Then do Numbers 12 through 22.

The Story of Daedalus: A Retelling of the Greek Myth

Daedalus was a Greek architect—a building designer—who was known for his ingenious inventions and projects. Daedalus designed, among other things, the Labyrinth, a maze of many paths. Famous throughout the world, the Labyrinth consisted of twisting paths from which it was impossible to escape. People entering the Labyrinth would find themselves wandering around and around forever.

Daedalus served as the architect for Minos, the king of Crete. Daedalus built the Labyrinth for Minos to imprison the monster called the Minotaur, who was half human and half bull. One day the hero Theseus offered to go into the Labyrinth to fight the Minotaur. Upon seeing Theseus, Minos's daughter Ariadne fell in love with him, and she begged Daedalus to help her make sure Theseus escaped from the Labyrinth.

GO ON

Daedalus told Ariadne to give Theseus a ball of thread to fasten to the door so that he could retrace his steps and find his way out after fighting the monster. Theseus was able to win the fight and, by following the thread, to escape the Labyrinth. Then he and Ariadne left Crete together.

When Minos learned that his daughter was gone, he became very angry with Daedalus. He put Daedalus and Daedalus's son, Icarus, in the maze. The Labyrinth was so cleverly designed that even Daedalus, its creator, could not find the way out. However, Daedalus did come up with a plan to escape. He and his son would flee through the air. With wings made out of wax and feathers, they would fly out of the maze. Before taking off, Daedalus warned Icarus to fly at a certain height over the sea. "If you fly too low, the waves will swallow you," said Daedalus. "If you fly too high, the sun will melt the wax, and you will fall into the sea."

Icarus agreed to fly safely between the sea and the sun, and they soared over the walls of the Labyrinth to freedom. However, as they continued on their flight, Icarus became more and more excited by the thrill of flying. He forgot his father's warning and flew higher and higher, paying no attention to Daedalus's pleas for him to fly lower. Flying too close to the sun, Icarus felt his wings melt and fall apart, and he fell into the sea. His heartbroken father flew safely to Sicily, where the king of Sicily welcomed him.

12 **Icarus can best be described as**

F very clever.

G very careless.

H a good student.

J a great hero.

13 **Why did Daedalus design the Labyrinth?**

A to imprison the monster called the Minotaur

B to help Theseus and Ariadne escape Crete

C to impress Minos with his cleverness

D to make Icarus proud of him

14 **Ariadne gave Theseus a ball of thread so he could**

F sew a magical coat to protect himself.

G weave a net to trap the Minotaur.

H make a rope to climb over the Labyrinth wall.

J find his way back out of the maze.

15 When Ariadne ran away, it caused Minos to

   A imprison Daedalus in the Labyrinth.

   B ask Daedalus to build a new Labyrinth.

   C decide to fight the Minotaur himself.

   D fly away from Crete to look for her.

16 Where did Daedalus and Icarus build their wings?

   F inside the Labyrinth

   G at Minos's palace

   H on board a ship

   J in Sicily

17 Which of the following occurred last in the story?

   A Icarus and Daedalus flew away.

   B Theseus fought the Minotaur.

   C Ariadne asked Daedalus for help.

   D Daedalus designed the Labyrinth.

18 The wax on Icarus's wings melted because

   F he flew over the maze wall.

   G his wings beat too fast.

   H he flew too close to the sun.

   J his father forgot to warn him.

19 How did Daedalus probably feel when he arrived in Sicily?

   A worried that the Minotaur might find him

   B excited to teach people to fly

   C sad that his son was not with him

   D honored to be able to meet the king

20 Which of these is a theme of the story?

   F Even kings can be poor in riches.

   G If you rush, you might do a bad job.

   H If you think hard enough, you can find a solution to a problem.

   J Hard work always pays off.

GO ON

21 The author's purpose in writing this selection was to

    A persuade readers to study Greek architecture and history.

    B give information about the history of flight in Greece.

    C explain how to build a variety of different structures.

    D provide a lesson about paying attention to advice.

22 Which word best describes Daedalus?

    F greedy

    G cheerful

    H creative

    J loyal

Directions

Write your answer to Question B on the lines below. Base your answer on the two selections you have read.

B Think about what Ichiro and Daedalus did in the two stories you read. In what ways do the two characters act similarly? Use details or examples from both stories to explain your answer.

WRITING ACROSS TEXTS

_____

_____

_____

_____

_____

_____

_____

_____

_____

_____

_____

PART 2: VOCABULARY

Directions
Mark your answer choice for Numbers 23 through 32.

23 What is the meaning of the homonym *swallow* in the following sentence?

If you fly too low, the waves will swallow you.

A believe too easily

B take into the stomach

C a small, swift bird

D take in

24 Which word pair contains antonyms?

F labyrinth – maze

G low – high

H fly – flown

J string – thread

25 Which of these correctly completes the following sentence?

While his mother talked, Ichiro paid close _____.

A attends

B attention

C attendance

D attendment

26 Which of these correctly completes the following sentence?

Ichiro's _____ grew as the day for the party approached.

F excitance

G excitation

H excited

J excitement

27 What does the word *just* mean in the following sentence?

His family had just moved to a new city.

A recently

B honest and fair

C at that moment

D exactly

28 What is the meaning of the homonym *flee* in the following sentence?

Daedalus and his son would flee through the air.

F escape from danger

G small jumping insect

H outdoor market

J unkind saying

29 Which word pair from "Ichiro's Tenth Birthday Party" contains antonyms?

A tried – impossible

B basketball – volleyball

C thrilled – forlorn

D brothers – uncles

30 Which of these correctly completes the following sentence?

Ichiro sent an _____ to each friend.

F invitement

G invitance

H inviting

J invitation

31 What does the word *courts* mean in the following sentence?

The activities center had a gymnasium with basketball and volleyball courts.

A places to play certain games

B the people around a king or queen

C places where legal decisions are made

D try to win favor with someone

GO ON

32 What does the word *ingenious* mean in the following sentence?

Daedalus was known for his ingenious inventions and projects.

F complicated

G expensive

H clever

J confusing

PART 3: WRITING CONVENTIONS

Directions
Mark your answer choice for Numbers 33 through 40.

33 Which of the following is a declarative sentence?

   A She took her dog on a long walk.

   B Why do dogs chase their tails?

   C Please be careful when opening the door.

   D How lucky she was to run into him!

34 Which of the following is an interrogative sentence?

   F This invention is the first of its kind!

   G Stop running next to the pool!

   H Would you go to the store for me?

   J Joseph had never seen a bear before.

35 Which of the following is an imperative sentence?

   A How do you learn to fly model airplanes?

   B She enjoys making things out of clay.

   C Hold the cup while I pour the tea.

   D It was the most beautiful sunset he had seen!

36 What is the subject of the following sentence?

   Sara wanted to leave the city.

   F Sara

   G wanted

   H to leave

   J the city

37 What is the complete predicate of the following sentence?

   The president, who wanted to spend time with his family, took a long vacation.

   A The president

   B who wanted to spend time

   C with his family

   D took a long vacation

GO ON

38 **Which group of words in the following sentence is a dependent clause?**

Yesterday morning, Sam slept late because there is no school on holidays.

F Yesterday morning

G Sam slept late

H because there is no school on holidays

J Sam slept late because there is no school on holidays

39 **Which of the following is a compound sentence?**

A Nathan and Loni played tennis all day.

B Pat opened the box, and Ramon closed it.

C Bharati wrote a letter, and sent it.

D Ms. Kim will grade the essays.

40 **Which sentence is written correctly?**

F Glacier national Park is in the Rocky mountains.

G She saw a Buffalo in Yellowstone National park.

H She went to a theme park in Buffalo, New York.

J The Blue ridge Mountains are in Virginia.

PART 4: WRITING

PROMPT

In both "Ichiro's Tenth Birthday Party" and "The Story of Daedalus," characters built unusual structures. Think about a time you built something such as a sand castle, a birdhouse, or a snow cave. Write a story about building this thing.

CHECKLIST FOR WRITERS

_____ Did I think about something I built?

_____ Did I put the events of my story in order?

_____ Did I use time-order words?

_____ Does my story have a beginning, middle, and end?

_____ Did I use words and details that clearly expressed my ideas?

_____ Do my sentences make sense?

_____ Did I check my sentences for proper grammar and punctuation?

_____ Did I check my spelling?

_____ Did I make sure my paper is the way I want readers to read it?

NAME _____ DATE _____

Scott Foresman
Benchmark Test
Unit 2
Doing the Right Thing

PEARSON

Glenview, Illinois
Boston, Massachusetts
Chandler, Arizona
Upper Saddle River, New Jersey

ISBN-13: 978-0-328-53752-5
ISBN-10:   0-328-53752-7

1 2 3 4 5 6 7 8 9 10 V011 19 18 17 16 15 14 13 12 11 10
CC1

ISBN-13: 978-0-328-53752-5
ISBN-10:   0-328-53752-7

PART 1: COMPREHENSION

Directions
Read about historic chess matches between a man and a machine, and learn how computers have improved at chess. Then do Numbers 1 through 11.

The Great Chess Match: Kasparov Versus Deep Blue

Back in 1950, some clever computer programmers began designing a computer to play chess. The first thing the programmers had to do was create a formula, or a step-by-step plan, for following the rules of chess. For the computer to be successful, however, it had to be programmed to solve the problems that come up during a game. The greatest problem for a chess player is keeping the valuable king piece safe at all times. When a player loses the king, that player loses, and the game is over.

The average person can consider only one or two chess positions per second. One big advantage the computer had was its ability to analyze many different chess positions very quickly. By 1988, programmers had created a computer named

Deep Thought that could search and consider the advantages and disadvantages of 750,000 positions per second. In 1989, Russian Garry Kasparov, who was the world chess champion at the time, agreed to play Deep Thought. Against the computer, the chess master was undefeated in a two-game match, and people were convinced that the machine was no match for human intelligence.

Six years later, Kasparov, who was still the world's chess champion, agreed to a six-game match against a new computer named Deep Blue. In the first game, Kasparov lost to Deep Blue in the thirty-seventh move of the game. After that first game, people were shocked, and many began to wonder if machines had become as smart as people.

As the match continued, however, Kasparov played differently, taking positions he knew the computer would have a hard time analyzing. After changing his game-playing strategy, Kasparov began winning, and eventually won the match with a final score of four games to two. Kasparov's victory showed that human intelligence still had the advantage of flexibility over machines.

1 **According to the selection, which of the following events occurred first?**

A   The computer Deep Blue was created.

B   The computer Deep Thought was created.

C   A world champion chess player lost a game to a computer.

D   Garry Kasparov agreed to a chess match with a computer.

2 **The phrase "Six years later" in the third paragraph helps the reader understand**

F   a cause-and-effect relationship.

G   the difference between a fact and an opinion.

H   the author's purpose.

J   the sequence of events.

3 **What happened after Kasparov changed his strategy in the match against Deep Blue?**

A   Deep Blue continued to beat Kasparov.

B   Computer programmers designed a new computer.

C   Kasparov began winning against the machine.

D   Kasparov decided computers were worthy opponents.

4 How did Kasparov change his strategy in the match against Deep Blue?

   F He gave up his playing pieces except for the king.

   G He asked a team of expert chess players to help with each move.

   H He played at a much faster pace to confuse the computer.

   J He selected moves the computer would have difficulty analyzing.

5 Based on the selection, how were Deep Blue and Kasparov alike?

   A They were both taught by scientists.

   B They had both defeated Deep Thought.

   C They were both highly skilled at chess.

   D They could both analyze thousands of plays per second.

6 Based on the selection, how were Deep Thought and Deep Blue different?

   F Deep Thought lost all its games against Kasparov; Deep Blue won some games against Kasparov.

   G Deep Thought was a computer; Deep Blue was a computer programmer.

   H Deep Thought won all of its games against Kasparov; Deep Blue won only some of its games against Kasparov.

   J Deep Thought was the nickname of a chess player; Deep Blue was the name of a computer.

7 Which of the following is a statement of opinion?

   A The average person can consider only two chess positions per second.

   B When a player loses a king, the chess game is over.

   C Kasparov is the greatest chess player who ever lived.

   D Kasparov lost to Deep Blue in the thirty-seventh move of the game.

8 Which of the following is a generalization that could be made from reading the selection?

   F Human minds are more flexible than computers.

   G The best chess players come from the United States.

   H Computers are generally much smarter than people.

   J Most computers were invented before 1950.

9 What happened after Kasparov beat Deep Thought in a chess match?

A Computer programmers gave up on designing chess-playing machines.

B People concluded that computers were no match for human intelligence.

C Kasparov decided to retire before he lost the world champion title.

D Deep Thought was redesigned to analyze a million positions per second.

10 The author probably wrote this selection to

F explain how to build a computer.

G tell about exciting games of chess.

H express personal feelings about computers.

J describe how to become a chess champion.

11 Based on the selection, how are people who play chess different from computers that play chess?

A People can analyze one or two chess positions per second, but computers can analyze thousands per second.

B People adapt more slowly than computers to different game strategies.

C Computers are better than people at keeping the king piece safe and winning games.

D Computers cannot play as many chess games in one day as people can.

GO ON

Directions

Write your answer to Question A on the lines below.

A In "The Great Chess Match: Kasparov Versus Deep Blue," Garry Kasparov won and lost games against a difficult challenger. Tell about a time you played a game against a difficult challenger and how you won or lost.

_____

_____

_____

_____

_____

_____

_____

_____

_____

Directions

Good friends Octavia and Andy each build a talented robot. Read about what
happens at the science fair. Then do Numbers 12 through 22.

A Tale of Two Robots

Octavia and Andy were fifth-graders in Mr. Arenstein's class, and they were
also best friends. Both fifth-graders liked science, and both of them were working
on projects for the science fair at their school. The theme of the science fair was
"Technology to Serve People."

Octavia knew she wanted to be a doctor when she grew up, and she decided to
make a robot that would be able to help people who weren't feeling well. Working
for several months, she programmed a robot that would check for fever by taking
a person's temperature. Her invention, which she named Doctor R, could also
monitor a heartbeat and pass out adhesive bandages to people who needed them.

Andy also built a robot, and, like Octavia, he based his design on his future
career choice: being a rock musician. Andy named his robot Rocky, programming it
to sing and play the guitar music for three different songs.

During the science fair, Octavia, Andy, and the other students brought their
hi-tech projects to the school gym and demonstrated them for the teachers and other
students. Although Octavia and Andy had worked separately, their robots looked

almost the same. Both Doctor R and Rocky were small, round machines made from old globes. Both robots moved on four spiky legs that were fashioned from metal pieces; both had two arms adapted from forks and other moveable pieces; and each robot had a single flashing light. "We can't even distinguish ourselves now. Looks like we were thinking along the same lines," Andy joked to Octavia.

"Visually, at least," she said, laughing.

Andy's robot, Rocky, was performing the song "Country Roads" when suddenly it fell off the small stage Andy had made. After seeing Rocky fall, Octavia used her remote control to send Doctor R speeding over to offer a bandage. "Take me home," sang Rocky. (It was a line from the song.) Everyone laughed and applauded.

Doctor R rolled back to Octavia. Rocky finished his song and bowed to the audience. The judges gave Octavia and Andy first prize to share. They congratulated both students on making functional robots that had amazed and amused everyone at the science fair.

12 **According to the story, which of the following occurred first?**

F The students laughed at Rocky.

G Octavia and Andy built robots.

H Doctor R delivered a bandage.

J Rocky fell off his stage.

13 **When did Doctor R offer Rocky a bandage?**

A after the judges gave out prizes

B while Andy was building Rocky

C after Rocky fell off the stage

D while Octavia was receiving first prize

14 **How did the appearance of Doctor R resemble that of Rocky?**

F They both had rectangular bodies.

G They both had several flashing lights.

H They were both made of old globes.

J They were both remote-controlled.

15 **How were Rocky and Doctor R different?**

A Rocky's hands were forks, whereas Doctor R's hands were spoons.

B Rocky acted like a musician, whereas Doctor R acted like a doctor.

C Rocky could bow to an audience, whereas Doctor R could not move.

D Rocky was built in one night, whereas Doctor R took months to build.

16 **What did Octavia and Andy base their robot designs on?**

F their favorite movies

G models they saw in a book

H their dream jobs

J characters in a comic strip

17 **Which word from the third paragraph is a clue word showing a comparison between Octavia and Andy?**

A built

B like

C design

D different

18 **Octavia can best be described as**

F thoughtful.

G musical.

H lazy.

J noisy.

19 **Where does most of the story take place?**

A in Octavia's garage

B in a classroom

C in a science laboratory

D in a school gym

GO ON

20 The author's purpose in writing this selection was to

    F   entertain with a story about two friends.

    G   give facts about student competitions.

    H   explain how to win a prize at a science fair.

    J   tell a story about the dangers of robots.

21 Which of the following is a theme of the selection?

    A   Friends often think alike.

    B   Everybody likes to make jokes.

    C   Robots are taking over the world.

    D   It takes perfection to succeed.

22 What was the climax of this story?

    F   The audience laughed.

    G   The robots looked alike.

    H   Doctor R helped Rocky.

    J   Rocky sang.

Directions

Write your answer to Question B on the lines below. Base your answer on the two selections you have read.

B In both selections, machines acted like human beings. Describe how Deep Blue, Doctor R, and Rocky behaved like people. Give details or examples from both selections to explain your answer.

WRITING ACROSS TEXTS

_____

_____

_____

_____

_____

_____

_____

_____

_____

_____

PART 2: VOCABULARY

Directions
Mark your answer choice for Numbers 23 through 32.

23 What does the prefix *dis-* in *disadvantages* mean in the following phrase?

"...consider the advantages and disadvantages of 750,000 positions..."

A before

B opposite of

C above

D ongoing

24 What does the prefix *un-* in *undefeated* mean in the following sentence?

Against the computer, the chess master was undefeated in a two-game match.

F always

G again

H not

J before

25 What does *analyzing* mean in the following sentence?

The computer would have a hard time analyzing these positions.

A completing

B programming

C winning

D studying

26 What does *flexibility* mean in the following sentence?

Kasparov's victory showed that human intelligence still had the advantage of flexibility over machines.

F ability to bend back and forth

G ability to meet new situations

H ability to spring back

J ability to stretch

Use this entry from a dictionary to answer Number 27.

---

monitor (mon´ətər), **1** *n.* pupil in school with special duties: *The hall monitor told the other students not to run in the hall.* **2** *n.* someone who gives advice or warning: *The monitor warned us not to swim in the deep water.* **3** *v.* to check; to keep track of: *The nurse was able to monitor the baby's breathing.* **4** *n.* screen on which a computer shows information and instructions: *The airplane monitor allowed the pilot to land safely.*

---

27 Which definition does *monitor* have in the following sentence?

   Doctor R was a robot that could monitor a person's heartbeat.

   A Definition 1
   B Definition 2
   C Definition 3
   D Definition 4

28 Between which guide word pages in the dictionary is *advantage* found?

   F adherent—administer
   G administrate—adopt
   H adoptive—advance
   J advanced—advice

29 Which word means about the same as *positions* in the following sentence?

   The average person can consider only one or two chess positions per second.

   A games
   B moves
   C strategies
   D pieces

30 What does the prefix *dis-* in *distinguish* mean in the following sentence?

   "We can't even distinguish ourselves now," joked Andy.

   F apart
   G with
   H again
   J for

GO ON

---

31 Which part of the dictionary entry explains how to pronounce *spiky?*

A spīʹkē

B *adj.*

C having sharp points (like nails)

D spikíˑer, spikíˑest

32 What does the word *functional* mean in the following sentence?

They congratulated both students on making functional robots.

F funny

G twin

H winning

J working

PART 3: WRITING CONVENTIONS

Directions
Mark your answer choice for Numbers 33 through 40.

33 Which of the following words is correct?

A citys

B cities

C vallies

D vallys

34 Which of the following is not a plural noun?

F children

G dresses

H women

J foot

35 Which of the following sentences is correct?

A Angela had lost two tooths.

B The drawer contains three knives.

C Please rake the leafs outside.

D A bunch of gooses flew overhead.

36 Which of the following sentences is correct?

F Shyam's geese doesn't fly.

G Pierre's feet were sore.

H Celia's bus are late.

J Lincoln's oxen is strong.

37 Which of the following sentences is correct?

A Miss. Shah will explain the problem.

B Mr Giardina is cleaning the sink.

C Ms. Riley will drive to the school.

D I have not seen Dr Cortez today.

38 Which of the following words should be capitalized?

F boy

G friends

H mexico

J television

39 Which of the following sentences uses all the proper nouns correctly?

A I'll see you after St. patrick's Days.

B When is Martin Luther King day?

C Sari opened the gift on Valentine's Day.

D Everyone shouted on new Year's Eve.

40 Which of the following sentences is correct?

F Martin had helped his father cook dinner.

G I had took Aunt Carol to the grocery store.

H She have boughten apples for her mother.

J They have went to the baseball game.

PART 4: WRITING

PROMPT

In both "The Great Chess Match" and "A Tale of Two Robots," people and characters used machines. Think about a machine you know how to operate. Write an explanation of the machine and how to use it. Include step-by-step instructions for someone to follow.

CHECKLIST FOR WRITERS

_____ Did I think about a machine I know how to use?

_____ Did I take notes about how to use the machine before I started writing?

_____ Did I write my explanation in the order in which steps are done?

_____ Did I use words and details that clearly expressed my ideas?

_____ Do my sentences make sense?

_____ Did I check my sentences for proper grammar and punctuation?

_____ Did I check my spelling?

_____ Did I make sure my paper is the way I want readers to read it?

NAME _____ DATE _____

Scott Foresman
Benchmark Test
Unit 3
Inventors and Artists

PEARSON

Glenview, Illinois
Boston, Massachusetts
Chandler, Arizona
Upper Saddle River, New Jersey

ISBN-13: 978-0-328-53753-2
ISBN-10:   0-328-53753-5

1 2 3 4 5 6 7 8 9 10 V011 19 18 17 16 15 14 13 12 11 10
CC1

ISBN-13: 978-0-328-53753-2
ISBN-10:   0-328-53753-5

*D*irections
Read about a famous poet and author who writes about people from different places. Then do Numbers 1 through 11.

Naomi Shihab Nye

Naomi Shihab Nye is an award-winning poet and author of books for both children and adults. She was born on March 12, 1952, in St. Louis, Missouri. Her father was born in Palestine, and her mother was born in the United States. Nye's books are often about making connections between people from different countries or cultures, such as in her own family.

Nye began writing when she was just six years old. Early on, she was fascinated by the power that books have to open up new points of view and introduce people to things they might not otherwise study or know about. Her first love was poetry, and she read and admired great poets such as Emily Dickinson, one of the most beloved of all American writers.

When she was seven years old, Nye published her first poem in a magazine called *Wee Wisdom*. She credits her second-grade teacher for making her read and memorize poetry. She also says the library was her friend as a child. Throughout her childhood, Nye published her writing in children's magazines and, later, in teen magazines.

During high school, Nye lived in Jerusalem, Israel, and in San Antonio, Texas. All the places she lived had a mix of different cultures and people with different customs. Nye loved these experiences. Her father was a newspaper writer, and her mother was a painter. So, she was constantly surrounded by art, and the artist's life came naturally to her.

One of Nye's books is *This Same Sky: A Collection of Poems from Around the World*. For this book, Nye gathered writing from people around the world, as the title states. By doing this, she hoped to help people in different countries come to know and understand each other better.

Nye's writing is simple, yet very beautiful. In her books, she often describes daily tasks, such as preparing a meal, knitting a sweater, or walking down a street. She writes about how people get along with each other, or how they don't get along with each other very well at times. She always includes the possibility that people can learn to respect each other, even if they start off with opposing ideas.

Naomi Shihab Nye believes reading and writing have the power to change people. She encourages everyone to read and write so they can get to know themselves better, and so they may come to understand others better too. The next time you go to the library, check out her books. They are well worth reading.

1 **What is the author's purpose in the first paragraph?**

A to persuade readers to read Naomi Shihab Nye's books

B to explain to readers who Naomi Shihab Nye is

C to introduce all the members of the writer's family

D to give information about Palestinians living in America

2 **What is the main idea of paragraphs 2 and 3?**

F *Wee Wisdom* is a poetry magazine for children.

G Nye's second-grade teacher liked poetry.

H Nye was young when she started to write.

J The library is a great place to get books.

3 Nye's mother and father got along despite what key difference?

A Her mother was from St. Louis; her father was from San Antonio.

B Her mother was from the United States; her father was from Palestine.

C Her mother was a painter; her father was a businessman.

D Her father used his imagination; her mother did not.

4 To inform you about Nye's work, the author

F presented one of Nye's poems.

G gave an example of one of Nye's books.

H listed the titles of all of Nye's books.

J compared Nye's books for children and adults.

5 Which sentence contains a statement of opinion?

A Her first love was poetry, and she read and admired great poets such as Emily Dickinson.

B Throughout her childhood, Nye published her writing in magazines.

C For this book, Nye gathered writing from people around the world, as the title states.

D One of Nye's books is *This Same Sky: A Collection of Poems from Around the World.*

6 Which sentence is a statement of fact?

F Naomi Shihab Nye's writing is simple, yet very beautiful.

G She was born on March 12, 1952.

H The next time you go to the library, check out her books.

J They are well worth reading.

7 According to the selection, Nye lived in all of the following places EXCEPT

A Jerusalem, Israel.

B St. Louis, Missouri.

C San Antonio, Texas.

D New Mexico.

8 Based on the selection, what did Nye love about all the places she lived?

F the teachers she had in school

G the other writers who lived there

H the hot climate

J the mix of different people

9 Which of the following would best help you prove that this statement of fact is true?

Naomi Shihab Nye's books have won awards.

A atlas

B card catalog

C biography

D dictionary

10 When did Nye get her first poem in a magazine?

F at six years old

G at seven years old

H as a teen

J as an adult

11 According to the selection, Nye mostly writes about

A people from different places who get to know each other.

B how to knit sweaters with different patterns.

C how to cook meals from the United States and Palestine.

D people from all around the world who like poetry.

GO ON

Directions

Write your answer to Question A on the lines below. Base your answer on "Naomi Shihab Nye."

A   Naomi Shihab Nye believes reading and writing have the power to change people. Explain how this might be possible.

_____

_____

_____

_____

_____

_____

_____

_____

_____

Directions

Every artist has a special way of expressing himself or herself, whether the art is photography, painting, writing, or sculpture. Learn about artist Michael Naranjo and his special way of creating art. Then do Numbers 12 through 22.

Please Touch

Mountain Spirit, by Michael Naranjo, 1995

  Imagine that you walk into an art museum to see an exhibit, and the first thing you see is a sign beside a sculpture of a hunter that reads, "Please Touch." You look around and notice that, in fact, every piece of art in this exhibit has a similar sign; you are astounded! You know that normally there is a uniformed guard in the gallery ready to holler, "Don't touch!" if anybody even comes close to the art. You wonder what's going on. Who changed the rules?

  The person who changed the rules—and actually wants visitors to touch his art—is Michael Naranjo, a famous Native American sculptor. Michael Naranjo wants visitors to experience his art in the same way that he makes it, through the sense of touch. Naranjo is blind, and he makes his statues by feeling them, not looking at them.

  Naranjo studied art in college and was blinded later, during his service in the Vietnam War. While he was recovering in the hospital, a worker gave him some

GO ON

clay to play with so that he could gain strength in his right hand, which had also been injured in the war. Naranjo was comfortable with shaping clay as his dream in college had been to become a sculptor. Almost without thinking, he molded the clay into a simple shape that looked like what it was meant to be. His dream of being a sculptor was reborn.

After getting out of the hospital, he returned home to Santa Fe, New Mexico, and began to train himself to make warriors and dancers, bears and deer, and fish and birds. He used his hands, his Native American culture, and his imagination to make his art. Completely by touch, Naranjo learned to tell whether his leaping elk had the right movement. He learned by touch if his dancer was graceful or if his eagle was balanced correctly for flight. He even traveled to famous museums in Europe and was given permission to touch their great works of art so he could learn from them.

Michael Naranjo's touchable art shows are similar to hands-on science exhibits at children's museums or to petting zoos where visitors can touch the animals. Naranjo enjoys asking visitors to experience art in a different way from how they usually do. The signs that say "Please Touch" also have descriptions of the sculptures, in print and Braille, the printed language for people who are blind. Included in each description is a reminder—"Use your imagination." Michael Naranjo taught himself to "see" with his hands and his imagination; now he is inspiring others to do the same.

12 **The main difference between Naranjo's art shows and most art shows is that visitors are asked to**

F keep their eyes closed.

G make their own art.

H meet and talk to the artist.

J experience the art through touch.

13 **What is the main subject of the fourth paragraph?**

A how Naranjo studies animals and his culture

B why Naranjo traveled to Europe to see art

C how Naranjo trained himself to make art

D why Naranjo decided to touch great works of art

14 **What interrupted Naranjo's dream of becoming a sculptor?**

F going to college

G working with clay

H being injured in battle

J traveling in Europe

15 Why did Naranjo have to get permission from museums in Europe?

    A   He wanted to touch their art, which was against museum rules.

    B   He wanted to arrange a meeting of artists at the museum.

    C   He needed a special guide because he was blind.

    D   He intended to spend more time than usual studying the art.

16 To which of the following did the author compare Naranjo's art shows?

    F   college classes

    G   schools for the blind

    H   petting zoos

    J   European museums

17 Which of these sentences is a statement of opinion?

    A   Michael Naranjo is a Native American.

    B   Naranjo's dancers would be more graceful if he could see them.

    C   Michael Naranjo studied art in college.

    D   While he was in the hospital, a worker gave Naranjo some clay.

18 Which of the following best shows that Naranjo was very determined?

    F   Naranjo is a Native American and a famous sculptor.

    G   He molded the clay into a simple shape.

    H   Naranjo wants the museum visitors to know what he knows.

    J   He began to train himself to make warriors and dancers.

19 Which of these statements contains BOTH fact and opinion?

    A   Naranjo's home is in Santa Fe, New Mexico.

    B   Naranjo makes art with Native American themes.

    C   Naranjo trained himself and therefore makes beautiful art.

    D   Naranjo's art is inspiring for the people who see it.

GO ON

20 According to the selection, which of these events happened first?

 F Naranjo lost his sight in a war.

 G Naranjo began to study art.

 H Naranjo had a show of touchable art.

 J Naranjo studied in European museums.

21 The author probably wrote the selection mainly to

 A encourage readers to try making clay art.

 B compare an art museum to a science museum.

 C persuade readers to attend Naranjo's show.

 D share information about Naranjo's achievements.

22 Based on the selection, which of these statements is a valid generalization?

 F Naranjo mostly makes statues of people.

 G Most museums do not give visitors permission to touch art.

 H There are many artists who are blind.

 J Most artists use themes from Native American culture.

Directions

Write your answer to Question B on the lines below. Base your answer on the two selections you have read.

B "Naomi Shihab Nye" and "Please Touch" present two different ways of learning. From each selection, give an example of something being learned, and tell how it is learned.

_____

_____

_____

_____

_____

_____

_____

_____

_____

_____

PART 2: VOCABULARY

Directions
Mark your answer choice for Numbers 23 through 32.

23 What is the meaning of the homonym *right* in the following sentence?

Naranjo learned to tell whether his leaping elk had the right movement.

A correct and fitting

B not curved

C opposite of left

D make letters with a pen

24 Which meaning of *exhibit* is used in the following sentence?

Michael Naranjo's touchable art exhibit is inspiring.

F evidence submitted to a court

G display or show

H demonstration

J sculpture

25 Which word is an antonym of *graceful*?

A solemn

B dainty

C slow

D awkward

26 What is the meaning of the homonym *great* in the following sentence?

Emily Dickinson is a great American poet.

F frame

G grind

H large

J remarkable

27 What is the meaning of *train* as used in the following sentence?

He began to train himself to make warriors and dancers, bear and deer, fish and birds.

A teach

B a series of thoughts

C practice for an athletic contest

D railroad cars pulled by an engine

28 What does the prefix *re-* in *reborn* mean in the following sentence?

His dream of being a sculptor was reborn.

F again

G back

H not

J before

29 What meaning of the word *sign* is used in the following sentence?

The first thing you see is a sign beside a sculpture of a hunter that reads, "Please Touch."

A public display of a message

B gesture that conveys information

C symbol with specific meaning

D write one's name on something

30 What is the meaning of *title* as used in the following sentence?

Nye gathered writing from people around the world, as the title states.

F a name for a royal person

G a claim to a house

H a name of a work

J a credit for a person in a film

31 The word *preparing* is made from the prefix *pre-* and the Latin root *pare,* meaning "to get ready." Thus, the word *preparing* means

A   getting ready again.

B   getting ready before.

C   getting ready later.

D   not getting ready.

32 Which sentence uses *so* correctly, as it is used in the following sentence?

So, she was constantly surrounded by art.

F   The so had ten piglets.

G   He needs to so a button on his jacket.

H   Ben was late, so I went to the movie alone.

J   She went to the garden to so lettuce seeds.

PART 3: WRITING CONVENTIONS

Directions

Mark your answer choice for Numbers 33 through 40.

For Numbers 33 to 35, mark the answer that best completes the sentence.

33   The raindrops _____ cold.
   A   fell
   B   felted
   C   felt
   D   feeled

34   Next week I _____ harder.
   F   had practiced
   G   will practice
   H   have practiced
   J   did practice

35   The teacher already _____ the lesson.
   A   had began
   B   beginned
   C   begun
   D   has begun

36   Which sentence is written correctly?
   F   Louis was sitting by the window, watching the snow.
   G   The students set quietly, waiting for the teacher.
   H   Sit the fence posts in a straight line.
   J   He told his dog to set.

GO ON

37 **Which sentence is written correctly?**

   A   Mr. Uchida was laying in his new hammock.

   B   Cory's watch lain under a pile of newspapers.

   C   Rosa laid awake worrying about the big game.

   D   The books were lying on the library table.

38 **Which sentence is written correctly?**

   F   The teacher called on Eva, but Simon answers.

   G   Lin cooked the eggs and then ate them.

   H   Hassan hears a knock, then opened the door.

   J   Kim's parents arrive on time, but left early.

39 **Which word in the following sentence is an object of a preposition?**

   After the picnic, Ramon sang the school song.

   A   picnic

   B   Ramon

   C   school

   D   song

40 **Which sentence is written correctly?**

   F   Mai done her work.

   G   Josh been sick a lot lately.

   H   Lily has been writing to me.

   J   Victor and Roxanne have did their best.

PART 4: WRITING

PROMPT

Books can make us think and answer our questions. Artwork helps us use our senses.

The works of authors and artists help make our lives more enjoyable by giving us information, entertainment, or fresh ways of looking at things.

Choose two works by one author or one artist, or one work by an author and one work by an artist. Compare the ways the works have affected you.

CHECKLIST FOR WRITERS

_____ Did I think about two works by an author, an artist, or an author and an artist?

_____ Did I take notes for my paper about the same and different ways they have affected me?

_____ Did I write my comparison in a way that shows the similarities and differences?

_____ Did I use words and details that clearly express my ideas?

_____ Do my sentences make sense?

_____ Did I check my sentences for proper grammar and punctuation?

_____ Did I check my spelling?

_____ Did I make sure my paper is the way I want readers to read it?

NAME _____ DATE _____

Scott Foresman
Benchmark Test
Unit 4
Adapting

PEARSON

Glenview, Illinois
Boston, Massachusetts
Chandler, Arizona
Upper Saddle River, New Jersey

ISBN-13: 978-0-328-53754-9
ISBN-10:   0-328-53754-3
1 2 3 4 5 6 7 8 9 10 V011 19 18 17 16 15 14 13 12 11 10
CC1

ISBN-13: 978-0-328-53754-9
ISBN-10:   0-328-53754-3

PART 1: COMPREHENSION

Directions
Austin and Kyle take a trip to Australia and encounter many new things. Read about their adventure. Then do Numbers 1 through 11.

Adapting in Australia

Austin and Kyle had just arrived in Darwin on Australia's northern coast. They were excited about visiting Kakadu National Park, but the flight from the United States had taken twenty hours, and they were tired.

Austin's stomach emitted a loud growl. He suggested finding something to eat. Near the harbor, Austin noticed a small shop that had a sign for pies.

"What kinds of pie do you have?" asked Austin.

The clerk said, "Let's see, we have potato and sausage, or steak and onion."

Austin blinked. Kyle gulped. "Do you have blueberry?" asked Austin slowly, with hesitation.

The man laughed. "Sorry, mate, all we sell here are meat pies."

Kyle ordered one of each as Austin looked at him questioningly. Kyle told him they might as well try them. As they devoured their food, which was tasty, they walked beside the harbor. They saw a sign with a diagram of a swimmer with a line through it, indicating that swimming was not allowed in the bay. They remembered that this area was home to the box jellyfish, or stinger. While many of the creatures are only the size of a grapefruit, their sting has been known to cause death.

Suddenly, they heard an eerie wail. Then there were barking and chirping sounds, followed by a long buzzing drone. Austin and Kyle hurried toward the noise.

They came to a shop with its door open. A man was standing inside, blowing into a long, stylish, wooden tube. This was the source of the strange and wonderful sounds.

The man said that the musical instrument was a didgeridoo. He explained that the instruments are usually made from tree parts that have been hollowed out by termites. The shopkeeper played another song for them, until Austin yawned and Kyle struggled to keep his eyes open. They said goodnight to their new friend and walked back to their hotel room for some much-needed sleep.

The next morning, they rode to Kakadu National Park, Australia's largest national park. A park ranger welcomed them.

He said, "We have quite a few of what we call 'tropical nasties' here at Kakadu. You don't want to miss the salty, also known as the saltwater crocodile, on your tour of the park. These reptiles can grow up to twenty feet in length, and they have been known to include humans in their diet. They're found in both salt and fresh water, so we don't recommend swimming here. There are other places where you can swim, though."

Kyle leaned over and whispered to Austin, "That's OK. My head is already swimming with all the new things I've seen and done in Australia."

1 **Why were Austin and Kyle tired when they arrived in Australia?**

A They were hot and hungry.

B They had been too excited to sleep.

C Their luggage was very heavy.

D Their flight had taken almost a whole day.

2 **How did the boys feel when they found out the shop sold meat pies?**

F excited

G angry

H surprised

J sad

3 Which of the following happened first?

A A man played a didgeridoo.

B The boys caught up on some sleep.

C A park ranger welcomed them.

D The boys visited the harbor.

4 Which of the following sentences answers why the author included dialogue in this selection?

F Dialogue makes the characters seem more natural.

G Dialogue makes it easier to understand the plot.

H Dialogue provides better descriptions of the action.

J Dialogue provides more clues about the characters' feelings.

5 Based on the selection, which generalization about Australia is valid?

A People in Australia are not very friendly.

B All interesting animals are found on land.

C Most activities in Australia take place indoors.

D There is much water in and around Australia.

6 Why did the boys walk toward the strange sounds they heard?

F They wanted to know what was making the sounds.

G They thought someone might be in trouble.

H They were in the mood to hear music.

J They were both musicians and hoped to join in.

7 Based on the selection, which generalization about Australia and the United States is valid?

A They are the same size.

B People listen to similar music.

C English is the main language.

D People eat the same kinds of food.

8 A reader might make this generalization:

Everything in Australia is dangerous.

Which detail from the selection shows that this generalization is false?

F Crocodiles have been known to kill people.

G There are some safe places to swim.

H Being stung by a box jellyfish can kill a person.

J Suddenly, they heard an eerie wail.

9 After the ranger said it was not safe to swim at Kakadu, Kyle said, "My mind is already swimming with all the new things I've seen and done in Australia." What does this suggest?

A He was ready to go home.

B He was not afraid of crocodiles.

C His plan was to swim after the ranger left.

D His thoughts were full of different experiences.

10 What can a reader conclude about Kyle and Austin?

F They were cousins.

G They liked learning about new things.

H They felt homesick.

J They were a little disappointed in Australia.

11 What was the author's main purpose for writing the selection?

A to convince readers to learn more about Australia

B to entertain with an amusing story about travel

C to explain how animals behave in Australia

D to give information about how to act in other countries

Directions

Write your answer to Question A on the lines below. Base your answer on "Adapting in Australia."

A The following is a generalization from the selection: "The boys were curious about their surroundings." What information in the selection supports this generalization?

_____

_____

_____

_____

_____

_____

_____

_____

_____

_____

Directions

We use our teeth every day, and not just for eating. Find out more about teeth and how animals and people use them. Then do Numbers 12 through 22.

Take a Bite of This

Teeth are the hardest and longest-lasting part of our body, so they're obviously important to our survival. Because we eat a variety of foods, we have different kinds of teeth for different uses. Some human teeth are for tearing, some are for chiseling, and others help us grind food. But are teeth only for chewing food?

Teeth also help us to speak properly and clearly. Count aloud quietly from one to four. What happened when you said "three"? You used your tongue and teeth to make the beginning sound, just as you did when you said "four," except this time you used your teeth and bottom lip. Your teeth were vital to forming the words correctly.

GO ON

Animals use their teeth for a multiplicity of tasks. Like people, they use them to eat. Some animals have long, sharp teeth that help them catch and hold onto prey. Animals can also use their teeth to build homes, carry objects, and defend themselves. Unlike people, animals often use their teeth as tools.

Animals that eat plants, such as deer and horses, have teeth in the front of their mouths that they use to saw through plants. They have large flat teeth in the back for grinding and mashing the leaves. Snakes' teeth slant backward, making it easier for them to swallow their prey. Some snakes have fangs with "holes" in them, through which venom drips when they're embedded in prey. A walrus's front teeth grow very long, allowing the animal to dig for shellfish and protect itself from other animals. A walrus can also use its long teeth as hooks when climbing on ice. An elephant's tusks are also teeth. They are used for protection, digging, and breaking branches.

People have two sets of teeth. The baby teeth are eventually replaced by permanent teeth. Some animals have many sets of teeth. African elephants go through six sets of teeth in a lifetime. If a shark loses one of its razor-sharp teeth, a new one quickly replaces it. Rodents, such as beavers, have one set of teeth that is constantly growing. Beavers use their teeth to chew through the trees they use to build dams and lodges. A beaver's teeth can grow four feet in a single year, so it's good they're constantly chewing.

Over time, living things go through changes, or adaptations, to help them survive in their surroundings. Because lions have to hunt for their food, their front teeth are very sharp and up to two inches long. On the other hand, animals that only eat insects, such as some types of bats, have special teeth that can crunch through the insects' hard shells. Teeth are one of nature's many marvels.

12 **What is the author's main purpose for writing the selection?**

F to demonstrate how nature works

G to convince readers to study animals

H to explain how animals' teeth differ from humans' teeth

J to encourage readers to care for their teeth

13 **The title of the selection is "Take a Bite of This." Which of the following would be the best alternative title?**

A "Don't Forget to Brush"

B "How Teeth Are Used"

C "What Dentists Do"

D "How Animals Survive"

14 Which of the following resources could be used to check this statement of fact?

Teeth also help us to speak properly.

F dictionary

G atlas

H thesaurus

J encyclopedia

15 What is one difference between people's teeth and animals' teeth?

A People have fewer sets of teeth than any animal does.

B People use their teeth to talk as well as eat.

C People's teeth are somewhat harder than animals' teeth.

D People's teeth last much longer than animals' teeth.

16 What helps a snake to hold and swallow its prey?

F Its teeth are slanted backward.

G Its teeth fall out very easily.

H Snake teeth have holes in them.

J The snake can poison its prey first.

17 Based on the selection, which of the following is a valid generalization?

A Teeth have many different purposes.

B All living things have sharp teeth.

C Teeth are best used for chewing.

D No animals have just one set of teeth.

18 What is the fourth paragraph mostly about?

F how animals poison their prey with teeth

G how animals with flat teeth eat

H why teeth called tusks are important

J how teeth differ depending on their use

19 Which of the following is a statement of opinion?

A Teeth are the hardest and longest-lasting part of the body.

B Animals can also use their teeth to build.

C It's a good thing beavers are constantly chewing.

D Animals that only eat insects have special teeth.

20 The major adaptations that are seen in people's teeth are related to

    F eating.

    G fighting.

    H protecting.

    J talking.

21 According to the last paragraph, why is it important for living things to be able to adapt?

    A Weather and other conditions are unpredictable.

    B If they experience no change, they lose the ability to adapt.

    C They may need several sets of teeth in a lifetime.

    D To survive, they must respond to changes in their surroundings.

22 The following statement is a faulty generalization:

All adult animals have permanent teeth.

What details in the selection let you know that this generalization is false?

    F African elephants go through several sets of adult teeth.

    G A walrus sometimes uses its teeth as hooks in order to climb.

    H Plant-eating animals have flat teeth for grinding leaves.

    J Rodents' teeth are always growing.

27 Based on the suffix *-tion,* what does the word *protection* mean in this sentence from "Take a Bite of This"?

The tusks are used for protection, digging, and breaking branches.

A in a state of being protected

B was protected in the past

C not protected

D to protect again

28 What is the meaning of *chiseling* in "Take a Bite of This"?

Some of our teeth are for chiseling.

F cheating

G striking

H cutting

J filing

29 Which meaning of *vital* is used in the second paragraph of "Take a Bite of This"?

A important

B deadly

C lively

D alive

30 What does *multiplicity* mean as used in this sentence from "Take a Bite of This"?

Animals use their teeth for a multiplicity of tasks.

F variety

G arrangement

H required set

J few kinds

31 Which word is a synonym for a walrus's *tusks?*

A trunks

B teeth

C roars

D whiskers

32 Which word is a synonym for *surroundings* as it is used in the last paragraph of "Take a Bite of This"?

F edges

G borders

H grassland

J environment

PART 3: WRITING CONVENTIONS

Directions

Mark your answer choice for Numbers 33 through 40.

33 **Which sentence is written correctly?**

A Who do you want to sing?

B Whom will sing next?

C Give it back to the one whom gave it to you.

D I know the person who asked to go.

34 **Which sentence is written correctly?**

F No one have eaten lunch yet.

G Are anybody listening to the rain?

H Everyone is excited about the concert.

J Everyone should buy their tickets early.

35 **Read this sentence:**

The queen waved.

If a pronoun is used in place of the noun, which of the following sentences is written correctly?

A She waved.

B They waved.

C We waved.

D It waved.

36 **Read the following sentences:**

The visitor ate a banana. She enjoyed it.

To which word does *it* refer?

F visitor

G ate

H banana

J She

GO ON

37 Choose the word that correctly completes the following:

Bob went home. _____ was tired.

A It

B Him

C His

D He

38 Which sentence contains a reflexive pronoun?

F Something is missing in this soup.

G Few were disappointed with the exhibit.

H I hope he doesn't hurt himself.

J Anybody can learn that trick easily.

39 Which sentence is written correctly?

A Him and me are friends.

B Him and I are friends.

C He and me are friends.

D He and I are friends.

40 Which sentence is written correctly?

F Joan shared she candy.

G Quinn lost his shoes.

H It is ours turn.

J Him dog is friendly.

PART 4: WRITING

PROMPT

Both "Adapting in Australia" and "Take a Bite of This" tell about changes that the characters and subjects experience. Think about a time that you or a person you know needed to change. Write a story about the change that was needed and what happened.

CHECKLIST FOR WRITERS

_____ Did I think about a time when a change was needed?

_____ Did I take notes about interesting events for my story before I started writing?

_____ Did I tell my story in the order in which it happened?

_____ Did I use words and details that clearly expressed my ideas?

_____ Do my sentences make sense?

_____ Did I check my sentences for proper grammar and punctuation?

_____ Did I check my spelling?

_____ Did I make sure my paper is the way I want readers to read it?

NAME _____ DATE _____

Scott Foresman
Benchmark Test

Unit 5
Adventures

PEARSON

Glenview, Illinois
Boston, Massachusetts
Chandler, Arizona
Upper Saddle River, New Jersey

ISBN-13: 978-0-328-53755-6
ISBN-10:   0-328-53755-1
1 2 3 4 5 6 7 8 9 10 V011 19 18 17 16 15 14 13 12 11 10
CC1

ISBN-13: 978-0-328-53755-6
ISBN-10:   0-328-53755-1

EAN

9 780328 537556

90000>

Directions
Read this account of an early cross-country trip by car. Then do Numbers
1 through 11.

Cross Country by Car

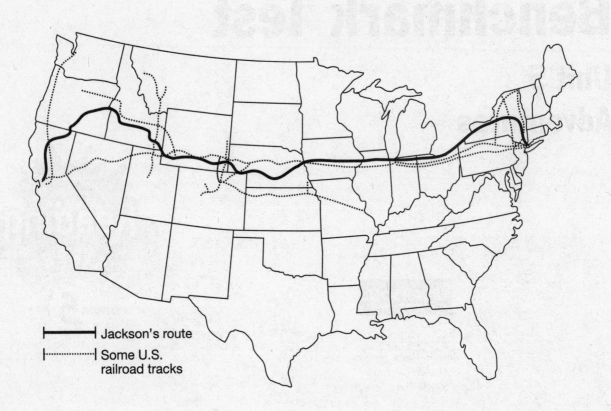

⊢━━━━⊣ Jackson's route

⊢┈┈┈┈┈⊣ Some U.S.
railroad tracks

Probably not a day goes by that we don't see or ride in a car, which makes it
hard to believe it's only been just a little more than one hundred years since the
first car trip across the United States. In 1903 a young man named Horatio Jackson
accepted a bet that an automobile could not be driven from California to New York
in less than three months. During a time when most people traveled in carriages
pulled by horses, this was an adventurous undertaking. There were no gas stations,
no road atlases, and only 150 miles of paved roads in the entire country!

The car's highest speed was thirty miles per hour, but most of the time it was
driven much slower than that. Parts of the car fell off during the rough drive, and it

had no top (nothing overhead) and no windshield. Jackson hired Sewall K. Crocker to be his mechanic and to help with the driving. Along the way, a stranger gave a young bulldog named Bud to Jackson. The two men wore goggles to keep dust out of their eyes—and so did Bud!

Jackson removed the car's back seat to allow more room for supplies, including sleeping bags, cooking utensils, warm clothes, and tools. Many nights he and Crocker camped out because they were in rural areas far from a town. They faced a variety of annoyances. They got stuck in sand and mud several times and had to pull or dig the car out. They drove back and forth, zigzagging, to find a way across gullies that had no bridges. When they had to cross a river, they endured a bouncy trip along a railroad trestle. They had to replace wheels and other parts over and over again. In addition, they caused a lot of excitement as they traveled. Sometimes people gave the men directions that took them out of their way. The people did this so that their relatives would have a chance to see an automobile for the first time. For many, the machine was incredible. Although there were no gas stations, general stores in most towns had fuel. The men and their mud-covered machine caused quite a sensation when they pulled into a new community.

The telegraph announced Jackson's approach to each town. As news of the adventure spread, two automobile companies sent out drivers to try to pass Jackson and get to New York first. However, Jackson was confident that he would beat them, and he did. Jackson, Crocker, and Bud traveled 5,600 miles in sixty-three days, helping to establish the automobile as a new reliable mode of transportation. Jackson never did collect on the original wager. Success must have been a sweeter reward!

1 **What is the author's main purpose for writing the selection?**

A to tell the story of the first cross-country car trip

B to entertain readers with details about the difficulties of traveling

C to explain the ways in which cars have changed over the years

D to convince readers of the fun of driving very long distances

2 **Which of the following is the most likely reason there were only 150 miles of paved roads in 1903?**

F Drivers only used their cars in and around cities.

G Cars were new and not yet widely used.

H Very few people knew how to pave roads.

J Many towns did not have the money to build roads.

3 **Why did Jackson and Crocker need to replace so many wheels and parts?**

 A   They were careless drivers.

 B   Their car was very old.

 C   The rough driving surfaces damaged the car.

 D   The car had been made with poor-quality materials.

4 **What was one result of driving on unpaved roads with no windshield?**

 F   It allowed Crocker and Jackson to go faster.

 G   Passengers and supplies fell out of the car.

 H   Crocker and Jackson were able to see the road more easily.

 J   A lot of dust got in the car and on the passengers.

5 **Read the following statement of fact from the selection:**

Jackson hired Sewall K. Crocker to be his mechanic and to help with the driving.

Which of the following resources could be used to check this statement of fact?

 A   a map of New York

 B   a dictionary

 C   a 1903 newspaper

 D   a thesaurus

6 **In the second paragraph of "Cross Country by Car," the author introduces a bulldog named Bud, who traveled with Jackson and his mechanic, and writes that the "two men wore goggles to keep the dust out of their eyes—and so did Bud!" Why did the author add this sentence?**

 F   to question the driver's decisions

 G   to provide background information about bulldogs

 H   to show what people found amusing back then

 J   to add an amusing detail about the car trip

7 **Why did two car companies send drivers to try to get to New York before Jackson?**

 A   It would be good for business if their cars were in the news.

 B   They did not like Jackson, so they wanted to beat him.

 C   It would make it easier for them to repair Jackson's car.

 D   They wanted to win the money from the bet.

8 At the end of the selection, what can the reader conclude about Jackson?

   F He was too angry to collect on the bet.

   G He was satisfied with what he had done.

   H He was an extremely forgetful man.

   J He was too ashamed to take the money.

9 The title of the selection is "Cross Country by Car." Which of the following would be best as an alternative title?

   A "Travels with Bud"

   B "Sleeping Under the Stars"

   C "American Travels"

   D "Road Trip!"

10 What does the dark black line represent on the map?

   F location of railroad tracks

   G route of the first car trip across the United States

   H borders of states

   J major rivers across the United States

11 Look at the map. What was the most likely reason this route was chosen?

   A It was near railroad tracks, which meant the men could get supplies.

   B The men did not have to worry about crossing any mountains.

   C It was the shortest distance between the East and West Coasts.

   D It included the most beautiful parts of the country.

Directions

Write your answer to Question A on the lines below. Base your answer on "Cross Country by Car."

A List two main ways that driving conditions today are different from driving conditions in 1903.

_____

_____

_____

_____

_____

_____

_____

_____

Directions

Read about two women trying to accomplish a childhood dream. Then do Numbers
12 through 22.

Making Dreams Come True

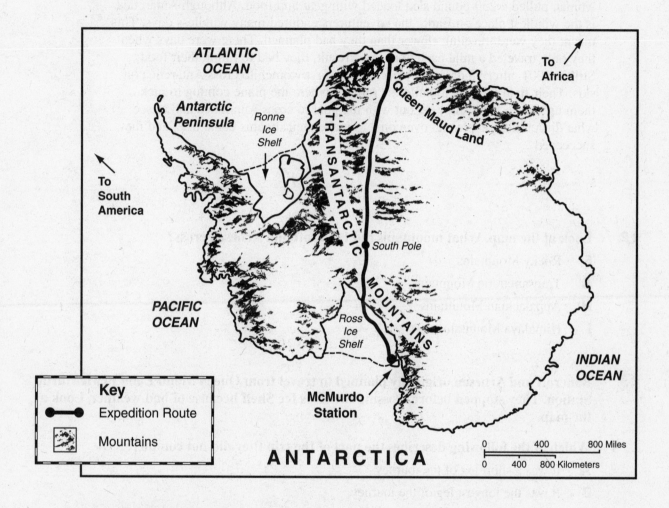

ATLANTIC
OCEAN

To
Africa

Antarctic
Peninsula

Ronne
Ice
Shelf

Queen Maud Land

TRANSANTARCTIC

To
South
America

South Pole

PACIFIC
OCEAN

Ross
Ice
Shelf

MOUNTAINS

INDIAN
OCEAN

McMurdo
Station

Key

Expedition Route

Mountains

0   400   800 Miles
0   400   800 Kilometers

ANTARCTICA

Ann Bancroft and Liv Arnesen grew up thousands of miles apart, yet they
shared a childhood dream. They each wanted to cross the frozen continent of
Antarctica. As adults they accomplished a number of feats. Bancroft climbed Mount
McKinley, the highest peak in North America. She was the first woman to ski
overland across Greenland, she traveled to the North Pole by dogsled, and she led a
team of women to the South Pole. Arnesen attempted to climb Mount Everest, the
highest mountain on Earth. She was the first woman to ski to the South Pole alone
and with no outside support. Following this event, Bancroft contacted Arnesen, and
the two began working together to realize their childhood dream.

Because they were traveling to such a difficult and faraway place, they had to
be tough and independent. They learned how to sew up wounds and what to do
in the event of a life-threatening injury. Bancroft spent some time in an ice cream

GO ON

freezer, where she tested her gear and tried to adapt to icy temperatures. They knew they would face winds up to one hundred miles per hour, and, indeed, they intended to use these winds to progress. The women would use wind-sails when the conditions were right to help propel them toward their goal.

Bancroft and Arnesen had only a hundred-day window of opportunity. Weather conditions for such a trip are uncomfortable year-round, but beyond this time, it would be too cold for an airplane to fly in to pick them up at journey's end. Each woman pulled a 250-pound sled loaded with gear and food. Although Antarctica is the windiest place on Earth, the adventurers endured many windless days. This meant they were traveling slower than they had planned. There were days when they only traveled a mile each hour. As a result, they had to ration their food. Still in 2001, after 93 days, they became the first women to cross Antarctica on skis. Their final job was to build the runway where the plane coming to pick them up was to land. They set out with the goal to cross Antarctica and to see what difficulties people can overcome to make their dreams come true, and they succeeded.

12   **Look at the map. What mountains did Bancroft and Arnesen cross?**

   F   Rocky Mountains

   G   Transantarctic Mountains

   H   Appalachian Mountains

   J   Himalaya Mountains

13   **Bancroft and Arnesen originally planned to travel from Queen Maud Land to McMurdo Station. They stopped before crossing the Ross Ice Shelf because of bad weather. Look at the map.**

   Which of the following describes the part of the trip they did not complete?

   A   It was a short leg of the journey.

   B   It was the longest leg of the journey.

   C   They would have had to cross water to get there.

   D   They needed to cross a peninsula to get there.

14   **What is the first paragraph mostly about?**

   F   the achievements of each of the women

   G   how Bancroft and Arnesen met

   H   how the women wanted to travel

   J   what inspired the women's childhood dreams

15 The author started the selection by saying that the women "grew up thousands of miles apart, yet they shared a childhood dream." Why did the author begin this way?

A to make the reader doubt they would ever meet

B to explain where each woman came from

C to show the reader that some meetings are planned well in advance

D to cleverly emphasize a difference before discussing a similarity

16 What did Bancroft and Arnesen have in common?

F Both enjoyed traveling with sled dogs.

G Both climbed Mount Everest.

H Both liked cold-weather adventure.

J Both experienced life-threatening injuries.

17 What caused the women to ration their food?

A Days without wind slowed them down.

B They wanted to split the food equally.

C Much of the food they brought couldn't be eaten.

D The plane carrying their supplies couldn't land.

18 Based on the selection, which of these is a valid generalization?

F Antarctica is a difficult but pleasant place to travel.

G Any healthy person could probably cross Antarctica on skis.

H Antarctica is safe to travel through for a short period of every year.

J Crossing Antarctica is probably the hardest thing these women ever did.

19 How did the women probably feel at the end of their journey?

A relieved and upset

B confused and lost

C exhausted and proud

D scared and nervous

GO ON

20 In this selection the most important details support

F skiing across Antarctica.

G first aid in winter.

H sliding and sailing.

J Liv Arnesen's journey.

21 What was the last thing the women did before leaving Antarctica?

A They went wind-sailing.

B They learned how to stitch injuries.

C They built a runway for the airplane.

D They tested their cold-weather gear.

22 What is the author's main purpose for writing this selection?

F to convince readers to become Antarctic adventurers

G to express feelings about Bancroft and Arnesen's journey

H to explain weather conditions at the South Pole

J to inform readers about the first women to cross Antarctica

Directions

Write your answer to Question B on the lines below. Base your answer on the two selections you have read.

B Describe at least two ways the people in "Cross Country by Car" were like the people in "Making Dreams Come True."

WRITING ACROSS TEXTS

_____

_____

_____

_____

_____

_____

_____

_____

_____

PART 2: VOCABULARY

*D*irections

Mark your answer choice for Numbers 23 through 32.

23 "Making Dreams Come True" tells of an uncomfortable trip across Antarctica. In other words, the trip was

  A not comfortable.

  B very comfortable.

  C most comfortable.

  D almost comfortable.

24 Bancroft and Arnesen were described as "tough and independent." What does the prefix *in-* mean in the word *independent*?

  F very

  G not

  H less

  J more

25 In "Making Dreams Come True," readers learn that Bancroft was "the first woman to ski overland across Greenland." What does the prefix *over-* mean in the word *overland*?

  A across

  B near

  C beside

  D beneath

26 What does *endured* mean in this sentence from "Making Dreams Come True"?

The adventurers endured many windless days.

  F thrived on

  G sailed in

  H lived through

  J hoped for

27 What does the prefix *re-* mean in the word *replace*?

  A under

  B within

  C again

  D above

28 Which of the following best explains the phrase "nothing overhead"?

F   The car had no roof.

G   The car had no windows.

H   The car was not in a garage.

J   The car was completely paid for.

29 "Cross Country by Car" states:

Jackson never did collect on the original wager that had been made.

What does *wager* mean in this sentence?

A   a bet

B   a salary

C   a race

D   an exchange

30 Which meaning of *sensation* is used in this sentence from "Cross Country by Car"?

The men and their mud-covered machine caused a sensation when they pulled into each new community.

F   feeling

G   crowd

H   thrill

J   success

31 Which of the following best describes the *telegraph* that announced the car's arrival in each town in "Cross Country by Car"?

A   a newspaper with local and national news

B   a radio network with many stations

C   a system that sent news great distances

D   a system for sending codes underground

32 What does the suffix *-able* mean in *reliable* in this sentence?

Jackson, Crocker, and Bud helped to establish the automobile as a new reliable mode of transportation.

F   lasting longer than

G   changing into

H   the opposite of

J   suitable for

PART 3: WRITING CONVENTIONS

Directions

Read the instructions and mark your answer choice for Numbers 33 through 40.

Read each sentence. Mark the answer that describes the underlined words.

33 The boy spoke <u>calmly</u>.

   A adjective

   B adverb

   C noun

   D verb

34 It is a <u>simple</u> problem.

   F noun

   G verb

   H adverb

   J adjective

35 The teacher is very <u>patient</u>.

   A adjective

   B verb

   C pronoun

   D noun

36 My brother will be here <u>soon</u>.

   F noun

   G verb

   H adverb

   J pronoun

Directions

Mark the answer that shows the correctly written sentence in each group.

37 **Which sentence is written correctly?**

A Her room is neater than his.

B She is the faster runner in her class.

C He is most careful than her.

D That pillow is soft than this one.

38 **Which sentence is written correctly?**

F Our team is gooder than your team.

G We have the most funniest teacher in the school.

H My brother is youngest than her brother.

J That is the dirtiest dog I've ever seen.

39 **Which sentence is written correctly?**

A Her brother is strongest than she is.

B She is the best singer in the group.

C That is the most happiest day of my life.

D My sister is more older than I am.

40 **Which sentence is written correctly?**

F This is the longer paper I've ever written.

G Rob is a slower runner than Tom.

H These socks are more drier than those.

J The old horse is more big than the young horse.

PART 4: WRITING

PROMPT

Both "Cross Country by Car" and "Making Dreams Come True" tell about adventures. Think about an adventure you would like to have with your classmates. Write a persuasive essay to convince your classmates to share the adventure with you.

CHECKLIST FOR WRITERS

_____ Did I think about an adventure I would like to have with my classmates?

_____ Did I make notes about why my classmates should share the adventure?

_____ Did I organize my paper in a logical way?

_____ Did I use words and details that clearly expressed my ideas, and that will persuade my classmates to come on the adventure?

_____ Do my sentences make sense?

_____ Did I check my sentences for proper grammar and punctuation?

_____ Did I check my spelling?

_____ Did I make sure my paper is the way I want readers to read it?

NAME _____ DATE _____

Scott Foresman
Benchmark Test
Unit 6
The Unexpected

PEARSON

Glenview, Illinois
Boston, Massachusetts
Chandler, Arizona
Upper Saddle River, New Jersey

ISBN-13: 978-0-328-53756-3
ISBN-10:   0-328-53756-X
1 2 3 4 5 6 7 8 9 10 V011 19 18 17 16 15 14 13 12 11 10
CC1

ISBN-13: 978-0-328-53756-3
ISBN-10:   0-328-53756-X

90000>

9 780328 537563

EAN

*D*irections
Meet Dean Kamen, an inventor who has a vision that he is making a reality. Read about several of his inventions. Then do Numbers 1 through 11.

Dreaming of a Better World

Dean Kamen's dreams are certainly big ones. He has produced more than 150 inventions, many of them related to health care. Kamen dreams of improving life for large groups of people. He has invented some amazing machines to make his own dreams and those of others a reality.

He invented a robotic wheelchair that can go up and down stairs. It can cross gravel and sand. It can raise its passenger so that he or she is as tall as someone who is standing. Kamen also invented a pump that allows patients to receive certain medicines without even being in a hospital. Instead of going to a hospital, people who need regular shots of medicine can wear a pump that provides them. This gives them much more freedom.

Most people in the world do not have access to clean water. When people drink dirty water, they get very sick. With this in mind, Kamen is working on a small engine that uses heat and cold to create energy. His goal is to put that engine in a small, portable machine that purifies water.

Kamen also knows that people need efficient, non polluting types of transportation. He invented a type of scooter called a Segway Human Transporter. This invention came after the robotic wheelchair, and it uses the same types of balancing sensors. The machine runs for a full day on about five cents' worth of electricity. It moves three to four times faster than a person can walk. So far, this machine has been used by postal workers and police officers. Kamen hopes that it will eventually be used by average citizens in large cities. And he dreams that it will help people in developing countries, where many cannot afford to buy cars and where pollution is a serious problem.

Beyond his role as an inventor, Kamen is a humanitarian, or someone who works to improve the lives of others. He hopes that his many successful inventions will inspire others to become interested and involved with technology that helps others. He created an organization called FIRST (For Inspiration and Recognition of Science and Technology). Each year, teams of students and engineers work together to build robots. Then the teams meet and compete with their robots, which must complete specific tasks. The event is both challenging and fun for students, and its popularity has grown tremendously. What started out in a high school gym with twenty-eight teams now takes place in large city parks with more than a thousand teams participating. The organization gives scholarships to the winners. Kamen's dream of inspiring other inventors is clearly becoming a reality.

---

1   **Based on this selection, which event happened first?**

    A   Teams competed with their robots in high school gyms.

    B   Kamen created the FIRST organization.

    C   Teams competed in large parks with their robots.

    D   Kamen gave scholarships to winners of robotic competitions.

---

2   **Based on the selection, which invention will be the last to be completed?**

    F   the robotic wheelchair

    G   the Segway scooter

    H   the water purifier engine

    J   the medicine pump

GO ON

3 Which of the following sentences is a statement of opinion?

A Dean Kamen's dreams are certainly big ones.

B He invented a robotic wheelchair that can go up and down stairs.

C The machine runs for a full day on about five cents' worth of electricity.

D Each year, teams of students and engineers work together to build robots.

4 How are the robotic wheelchair and the Segway alike?

F They are both related to health care.

G They can raise their passengers up to see better.

H They can be used instead of cars in busy cities.

J They use the same kind of sensors for balancing.

5 Which word best describes Dean Kamen?

A humble

B brave

C satisfied

D creative

6 Why is the Segway good for the environment?

F It is made from recycled parts.

G It uses a non polluting source of energy.

H It gives people more freedom.

J It travels faster than people can walk.

7 Why did Kamen create the organization called FIRST?

A He was tired of working on inventions.

B He wanted to be in a teaching environment.

C He hoped to interest young people in science and technology.

D He wanted to give out grants for research in technology.

8 Why has FIRST become so popular?

F Schools encourage students to participate.

G Students like to compete against each other.

H It receives funding and other support from the government.

J Students find the event exciting and enjoy participating.

9 What is the next-to-last paragraph mostly about?

  A what the Segway is

  B how to use the Segway

  C how the Segway is built

  D when the Segway was made

10 The title of the selection is "Dreaming of a Better World." Which of the following would be the best alternative title?

  F "A Modern-Day Inventor"

  G "Science and Technology"

  H "Inventions for Health Care"

  J "Today's Robots"

11 What is the author's main purpose for writing this selection?

  A to teach readers how to make a robot

  B to share feelings about a person's dreams

  C to tell about a man's ideas and accomplishments

  D to convince readers to learn about science and technology

Directions

Write your answer to Question A on the lines below. Base your answer on "Dreaming of a Better World."

A How do you know Dean Kamen is concerned about others? Describe two things Kamen has done for the benefit of other people.

_____

_____

_____

_____

_____

_____

_____

_____

_____

*D*irections

Read about Sydney's creative problem-solving on the way to visit her aunt. Then do Numbers 12 through 22.

A Creative Mind

Sydney and her parents loaded the trunk with their luggage and then returned to the house to see whether they had left anything behind. When they were satisfied that everything was packed, they got into the car to begin the long journey that would be Sydney's first visit with her Aunt Elena.

The sun's merciless rays blazed through the passenger window where Sydney was sitting. She felt the temperature rise and wondered what she could do to block the sun. First, she held a small towel up against the window glass, but she became uncomfortable sitting in one position with her arm raised. Next, she rolled the window down a fraction and hung the top inch of the towel outside, and then she shut the window so that it was holding the towel in place. This worked better than her previous solution, but she was still dissatisfied. The air streaming through the top of the window was noisy and bothersome.

GO ON

Her mother had packed construction paper, markers, and tape. Sydney decided to replace the towel with a maroon sheet of paper she taped to the inside of her window. This blocked the sun, but now she couldn't see the scenic countryside. She cut a small rectangle out of the paper to block most of the sun but still allow for a view of the scenery. The Blue Ridge Mountains and Shenandoah Valley were just too beautiful to miss.

After riding in the car for several hours, Sydney began to feel restless and wanted some entertainment. She cut twenty 3-inch squares from a yellow sheet of paper. Then she numbered them from one to ten, marking two squares with each number. Next, she shuffled the cards and placed them facedown on the seat beside her. She turned two cards over at a time, trying to find matching numbers. Each time she made a pair, she set them aside.

By the time she finished her second game, her father was preparing to park the car in Aunt Elena's driveway.

That evening over dinner, Sydney's parents bragged about her creativity and problem-solving abilities on the long ride. Her aunt chuckled softly and said, "She must get that from her parents."

12 **Which of the following happened first?**

F Sydney taped colored paper to the window.

G Sydney felt hot with the sun shining on her.

H Sydney held a towel against the window.

J Sydney viewed the Blue Ridge Mountains.

13 **Which of the following best describes Sydney's parents?**

A They are scientific thinkers.

B They expect Sydney to amuse herself.

C They are proud of Sydney.

D They enjoy taking long trips.

14 **The following statement is a faulty generalization:**

Sydney is never good at entertaining herself.

Which of the following details from the story lets you know this generalization is false?

F Sydney cut out a small rectangle to look through.

G Sydney used a towel to block the sun.

H Sydney created a game from just paper.

J Sydney was impatient to reach Aunt Elena's house.

15 What can you conclude about Sydney?

   A   She likes math and science.

   B   She takes care of problems by herself.

   C   She will be successful when she grows up.

   D   She does not travel often.

16 Sydney would probably make a very good

   F   dancer.

   G   scientist.

   H   police officer.

   J   newspaper reporter.

17 In what way is the long drive important to the plot?

   A   It allows time for Sydney to experiment.

   B   It affects the characters' moods in the story.

   C   It lets the reader know where the family is traveling.

   D   It explains why Sydney has not visited Aunt Elena before.

18 How does the reader know the conflict in the story is resolved?

   F   Aunt Elena tells Sydney she is like her parents.

   G   The family takes a trip to see Sydney's Aunt Elena.

   H   Sydney and her parents arrive at Aunt Elena's house.

   J   The family checks to make sure they have packed everything.

19 Which of the following is probably true of Sydney's parents?

   A   They are both artistic.

   B   They plan carefully.

   C   They like to exercise after driving.

   D   They have been married many years.

20 Which of the following did Sydney do last?

   F   She set aside the last pair of matched cards.

   G   She cut a rectangle out of a sheet of paper.

   H   She cut a sheet of paper into squares.

   J   She started a second game of cards.

GO ON

21   **What is the most likely reason the author wrote this story?**

A   to explain how to be a good traveler

B   to convince readers to be more thoughtful

C   to give readers ideas for making up games

D   to describe the creative activities of a girl

22   **What is the theme of the story?**

F   You can find solutions with help from others.

G   It can take more than one try to solve a problem.

H   Visit your relatives as often as you can.

J   Make sure you have everything you need.

Directions

Write your answer to Question B on the lines below. Base your answer on the two selections you have read.

B Describe at least one way Dean Kamen and Sydney are alike and one way they are different from each other.

_____

_____

_____

_____

_____

_____

_____

_____

_____

PART 2: VOCABULARY

Directions
Mark your answer choice for Numbers 23 through 32.

23 What is the meaning of *successful* in the following sentence?

> *Kamen hopes that his many successful inventions will inspire others to become interested and involved with technology that helps others.*

A   losing success

B   repeating success

C   without success

D   having success

24 What is the meaning of *uncomfortable* in the following sentence?

> *She became uncomfortable sitting in one position with her arm raised.*

F   not able to feel at ease

G   the state of being relaxed

H   having trouble

J   not tired

25 What is the meaning of *purifies* in the following sentence?

> *His goal is to put that engine in a small, portable machine that purifies water.*

A   creates

B   cleans

C   pours

D   measures

26 Which dictionary definition of *access* is used in the following sentence?

> *Most people in the world do not have access to clean water.*

F   use of important information

G   the means to get something

H   the desire to have something

J   an entrance to a building

27 What does the suffix in the word *hopeful* mean?

A having

B without

C showing again

D that amount

28 What does *merciless* mean in the following sentence?

The sun's merciless rays blazed through the passenger window.

F having new mercy

G full of mercy

H shows a little mercy

J without mercy

29 Which meaning of *block* is used in the following sentence?

She cut a small rectangle out of the paper to block most of the sun.

A a solid piece of a hard material

B stop the sight of something

C an area in a city with streets on all sides

D shape into solid pieces

30 Between which dictionary guide words would the word *previous* be found?

F predicate—preference

G premeditation—presentation

H presentative—pressure

J pretermit—price

31 What does *restless* mean in the following sentence?

Sydney began to feel restless and wanted some entertainment.

A the state of being quiet

B peaceful

C having slept well

D unable to relax

GO ON

32 **Which part of the dictionary entry shows how to say the word *Shenandoah?***

F   a scenic area in northern Virginia

G   a river flowing from northern Virginia

H   shen´ən dō´ə

J   shelter—shift

PART 3: WRITING CONVENTIONS

Directions
Mark your answer choice for Numbers 33 through 40.

33 **Which sentence is written correctly?**

    A Where are you going? she asked.

    B He said, What time do we leave?

    C They yelled, "We're number one!"

    D James asked "when my birthday was."

34 **Which sentence is written correctly?**

    F Her family visited, Austin Texas.

    G The party is December, 1, 2006.

    H Larry Paolo, and, Tori went to a movie.

    J As usual, she lost her keys.

35 **Which sentence is written correctly?**

    A He will be here, Saturday May 6.

    B Her cat is gray, white, and black.

    C My black dog Shadow, ran around the house.

    D My friend moved to Sedona Arizona.

36 **Which sentence uses a semicolon (;) correctly?**

    F It rained lightly; however, we were able to have our field day.

    G On our trip we saw the following; elk, bison, antelope, and moose.

    H He bought long string beans; Cortland apples; and summer squash.

    J We arrived back home long after 8;30 in the evening.

GO ON

37 **Which sentence is written correctly?**

A He loves apples, or oranges.

B Carlo and Amber came to visit.

C Salem Oregon is a northwestern city.

D Her two favorite activities are, biking and running.

38 **Which sentence is written correctly?**

F The paint looked brightly.

G The paint was brightly.

H The wind blew strong.

J The wind was strong.

39 **Read the following sentences:**

Drake was asleep. Bekka wanted to play.

Which sentence combines the two sentences correctly?

A Drake was asleep, but Bekka wanted to play.

B Drake was asleep or Bekka wanted to play.

C Drake was asleep, Bekka wanted to play.

D Drake was asleep because Bekka wanted to play.

40 **What is the misplaced modifier in the following sentence?**

Across the bridge we saw a man with a horse wearing pants that were baggy.

F Across the bridge

G with a horse

H wearing pants that were baggy

J that were baggy

PART 4: WRITING

PROMPT

Both inventor Dean Kamen and Sydney used their imaginations to solve problems. Think about a problem you have faced. Write an essay that describes the problem and what you did to solve it.

CHECKLIST FOR WRITERS

_____ Did I think about a problem I have faced and how I solved it?

_____ Did I list what I know about the problem before I started writing?

_____ Did I organize my essay in a logical way?

_____ Did I use clear words and specific details to describe the problem and its solution?

_____ Do my sentences make sense?

_____ Did I check my sentences for proper grammar and punctuation?

_____ Did I check my spelling?

_____ Did I make sure my paper is the way I want readers to read it?

NAME _____ DATE _____

Scott Foresman
Benchmark Test
End-of-Year

Glenview, Illinois
Boston, Massachusetts
Chandler, Arizona
Upper Saddle River, New Jersey

Reading STREET Grade 5

ISBN-13: 978-0-328-53757-0
ISBN-10:   0-328-53757-8
1 2 3 4 5 6 7 8 9 10 V011 19 18 17 16 15 14 13 12 11 10
CC1

ISBN-13: 978-0-328-53757-0
ISBN-10:   0-328-53757-8

EAN

9 780328 537570

90000>

Directions

If you think that young people cannot make a difference in the world, read this selection. Then answer Numbers 1 through 11.

Working for the Future

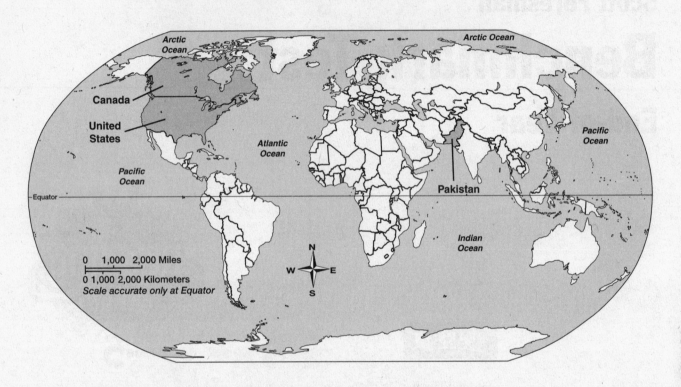

Don't tell Craig Kielburger that children don't have the power to make a difference in the world today, because he knows that isn't true. Kielburger grew up in Canada. When he was twelve years old, in 1995, Kielburger was searching for the comics page in the newspaper when he came upon an article about a twelve-year-old boy in Pakistan. This boy had been forced to work since he was four years old. Kielburger was affected by this stranger's difficult life, and he felt that he had to do something to try to change unfair labor practices in the world. He talked to some of his classmates, and together they started an organization called Free the Children.

Free the Children has several goals. One goal is to free children from poverty and unfair labor practices. Another goal is to encourage children everywhere to believe that they can make a difference in the world. When Kielburger speaks to youth groups, he tells them that even the smallest action can have an impact. He explains to young people that they can become leaders and help improve the world.

Kielburger speaks with the voice of experience. He has traveled to more than forty countries to visit children who are forced to work. He shares their stories, speaking out in defense of children's rights. In addition, Kielburger has met with many world leaders, co-written four books, and appeared on popular television programs such as *60 Minutes* and *Oprah* to discuss his work.

Kielburger believes that education is a critical way to break the cycle of poverty. The organization he founded, Free the Children, has built 350 schools around the world. The group Kielburger started in 1995 now has more than 100,000 youth representatives under eighteen years of age from thirty-five countries. Kielburger says his older brother Marc inspired him to work at making the world a better place. When Marc was twelve years old, he collected signatures for a petition to ban products that were harmful to the environment. Witnessing his brother Marc's passion and involvement in an issue that was important to him showed Craig that it doesn't matter how young a person is. Everyone has something to share, and each person can make a difference.

Despite the fact that Craig Kielburger has met many famous people, he says his heroes are the children he has met during his travels because they never give up hope. Kielburger himself has inspired hope in the many people whose lives he has touched through his tireless efforts to help.

1 **According to the selection, what happened first?**

A   Kielburger formed Free the Children.

B   Kielburger read about a child laborer.

C   Kielburger traveled around the world.

D   Kielburger co-authored four books.

2 **Which word best describes Kielburger?**

F   humble

G   wealthy

H   lonely

J   competitive

3 **What first caused Kielburger to realize young people could help solve problems?**

A   meeting with world leaders

B   the success of Free the Children

C   reading about a boy working in Pakistan

D   his brother's work trying to change things

GO ON

4 Which of the following contains a statement of opinion?

F Kielburger grew up in Canada.

G He has traveled to more than forty countries.

H The organization he founded, Free the Children, has built 350 schools around the world.

J Kielburger believes that education is a beneficial way to break the cycle of poverty.

5 What is a likely reason that most active members of Free the Children are under the age of eighteen?

A Adults are not interested in the organization.

B Many young people want to get involved with the group.

C It is an organization of young people for young people.

D Only child laborers are allowed to join the group.

6 Based on this selection, which of the following statements is a valid generalization?

F Many of the children Kielburger has met have inspired him.

G Pakistan has the highest number of child laborers.

H Most of the members of Free the Children live in the United States.

J The leaders Kielburger talked to were not concerned about child labor.

7 The title of the selection is "Working for the Future." Which of the following is the best alternative title?

A "Craig and Marc: Brothers and Friends"

B "Making a Difference"

C "The Importance of Schools"

D "Why You Should Read the Newspaper"

8 How are Craig Kielburger and his brother Marc alike?

F They are good students.

G They want to be world leaders.

H They take action to change things.

J They think children are the best leaders.

9 **What is the main idea of the selection?**

   A   People make a lot of mistakes.

   B   Children should lead the world.

   C   Anyone can contribute to change.

   D   Work in other countries is very hard.

10 **Look at the map. Which of the following is true?**

   F   Pakistan is part of Africa.

   G   Canada and Pakistan are neighbors.

   H   Pakistan is far away from Canada.

   J   Canada and Pakistan are about the same size.

11 **What was the author's main purpose for writing the selection?**

   A   to share the inspiring effects of one boy's actions

   B   to convince readers to join Free the Children

   C   to entertain readers with an amusing story

   D   to express feelings of pride about Canada

People immigrating to the United States from Europe traveled through Ellis Island on the East Coast. Read this story about Angel Island, the entrance for Chinese immigrants on the West Coast. Then answer Numbers 12 through 22.

A Trip Back in Time

Winsie zipped her backpack and ran downstairs excitedly. She had never been to Angel Island before. Her parents had explained that Angel Island Immigration Station was a historic landmark. Like Ellis Island on the East Coast, Angel Island was a place where immigrants were questioned before they were allowed to enter the United States. However, in 1882, the United States passed a harsh and controversial law that made it difficult for Chinese immigrants to enter the country. As a result, they were kept for weeks, months, sometimes even years in crowded buildings on Angel Island. Some of these people were not allowed to enter the new homeland they had dreamed of and were sent back to China.

Many of the people who were detained on Angel Island wrote and carved their thoughts and feelings on the walls, telling their stories of difficulty and confusion.

The walls of the buildings became a journal of the immigrants' frustration, sadness, boredom, and anger.

Although Winsie's mother had never heard any stories about Angel Island directly from her grandparents, she had learned through research that her grandfather had been held there for many weeks in 1930. She wanted to go and see where Pang Chen, her grandfather and Winsie's great-grandfather, had been forced to wait, wondering if he would ever be allowed to enter the United States.

Winsie and her parents took a boat across San Francisco Bay to reach the island, where they joined a guided tour and learned that the Immigration Station had operated from 1910 to 1940. Once the station was no longer in use, it was scheduled to be torn down. However, a park ranger found the poems and notes on the walls, and he organized a group of people who influenced the government to save the important buildings.

After the tour ended, Winsie and her parents wandered around inside one of the buildings. Suddenly, Winsie's father yelled, "Come look at this!" Winsie and her mother hurried to where he stood pointing at the wall. Winsie did not recognize the Chinese characters, but her mother and father excitedly agreed that they spelled out "Pang Chen, 1930." Suddenly, Winsie's mother began to cry, thinking of the sadness her grandfather and so many others had experienced here. Winsie pulled out a piece of white paper and a black crayon from her backpack. As her parents watched quietly, Winsie held the paper over the characters carved in the wall and rubbed the crayon gently back and forth until the characters showed up on the paper. After she had finished, she held the paper out for her mother, saying, "You should have Pang Chen's words always. I'm so happy he made a home here in the United States for himself, and for us."

12 **Which of the following happened last?**

F Winsie joined a guided tour.

G Winsie's father found Pang Chen's name.

H Winsie and her parents rode a boat to Angel Island.

J Winsie packed her backpack with things she might need.

13 **Which word best describes Winsie?**

A mischievous

B talkative

C prepared

D obedient

14 **What was the climax of the story?**

F Winsie's mother found out about Pang Chen.

G Pang Chen was held on Angel Island.

H Winsie's father found Pang Chen's name.

J Winsie learned the history of the island.

15 **The last paragraph is mainly about**

A Winsie making a rubbing of Chinese characters on a wall.

B Winsie's parents being able to read Chinese characters.

C the sadness Winsie's mother felt seeing Pang Chen's name.

D discovering and copying something Pang Chen had written.

16 **Which of these is a theme of the story?**

F Family trips are important.

G The past is powerful.

H Art comes in many forms.

J Laws are often unfair.

17 **How are Angel Island and Ellis Island alike?**

A Immigrants were checked there before entering the United States.

B Immigrants named these islands based on their experiences there.

C They are both on the country's West Coast.

D They were used only for Chinese immigrants.

18 **What was the main reason Winsie's mother wanted to go to Angel Island?**

F She had never been there before.

G She wanted Winsie to ride across San Francisco Bay.

H She had grown up hearing stories about her grandfather's stay there.

J She wanted to see where her grandfather had once been.

19 **How did Winsie's mother probably feel when Winsie gave her the wall rubbing?**

A grateful

B curious

C confused

D worried

20   What is the most likely reason Pang Chen wrote in Chinese characters?

   F   He did not want anyone to read his writing.

   G   He knew his Chinese granddaughter would see his message.

   H   He probably did not yet know the English alphabet.

   J   He found the characters easier to carve than letters.

21   Why did people want to save the buildings on Angel Island?

   A   The buildings had a unique design.

   B   A few immigrants were still living there.

   C   The buildings helped block storms from reaching the mainland.

   D   The buildings contained firsthand accounts of historic events.

22   What was the author's main purpose for writing this selection?

   F   to teach the importance of protecting historic buildings

   G   to describe the pain all immigrants experienced

   H   to entertain readers with a heartwarming story

   J   to convince readers to learn about their own families

GO ON

Directions

Write your answer to Question A on the lines below. Base your answer on the two selections you have read.

A Think about the main characters in the two selections you have read, "Working for the Future" and "A Trip Back in Time." Name at least one way Craig Kielburger and Winsie are alike and one way they differ from each other.

WRITING ACROSS TEXTS

_____

_____

_____

_____

_____

_____

_____

_____

_____

_____

D*irections*

Read about one way of communicating on the Internet. It's called blogging. Then answer Numbers 23 through 33.

What's New on the Internet?

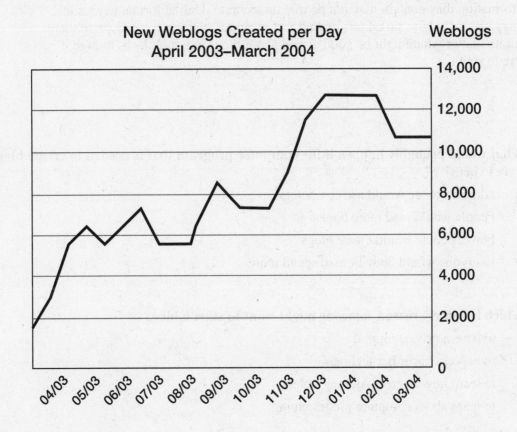

New Weblogs Created per Day
April 2003–March 2004

Weblogs

What is the odd name for a very popular activity that has taken the Internet by storm? It is blogging! *Blog* is a shortened combination of the words *web* and *log*. A blog is a type of personal journal posted on the Internet.

Just how popular is blogging? There are millions of blogs today, and new ones are created all the time. Their popularity continues to grow, in part because the program needed to create a blog is either free or very cheap. It is also, as computer folks often say, "user friendly."

A blog is an easy-to-use Web site where a person can express his or her thoughts. It is also a way to communicate with others, since many blogs have links to e-mail. This way, a person who is reading a blog can write a note to the person who owns the blog. Some businesses support blogs at work because of their ability to create large amounts of information that can be shared among workers. These are called "k-logs" or knowledge logs. Blogs are also used by colleges. In this case, blogs allow students to interact with teachers and classmates without having to wait to get back to the classroom. Blogging is also a way to give instant news on events while they are happening.

GO ON

Clearly, not all blogs are created equal. Some are simply a person's thoughts, which may or may not hold any value for a reader. However, others are posted by well-known reporters and contain breaking news. There are also blogs that provide helpful information, such as the best way to grow African violets or where to find free outdoor events.

People can use blogs to let others know about goods and services that are for sale. People can also use blogs in an attempt to shape public opinion, or to change the way people feel about certain things. One weakness of blogs is the fact that the information they contain may not be true or accurate. Unlike formal news sites, blogs generally have no editors and no fact-checkers making corrections to them. But no matter what might be good or bad about blogging, it looks as though it is here to stay.

23 **What would probably happen if the computer program that is needed to create blogs were expensive?**

A Almost no one would use computers.

B People would read more books.

C Fewer people would create blogs.

D Everyone would be willing to spend more.

24 **Which is a likely reason someone might want to start a blog?**

F to have a private journal

G to express his or her feelings

H to learn how to grow African violets

J to learn about computer programming

25 **The first sentence is "What is the odd name for a very popular activity that has taken the Internet by storm?" What does it mean to take something *by storm?***

A to remain mysterious

B to describe in great detail

C to become important suddenly

D to destroy violently

26 Which of the following is a statement of opinion?

F There are more than eight million blogs.

G Some businesses support blogs at work.

H Many blogs have links to e-mail.

J Clearly, not all blogs are created equal.

27 How do news sites and blogs differ?

A Blogs are often not accurate.

B News sites have a plain design.

C Blogs do not contain news.

D News sites are more interesting.

28 Which is a valid generalization based on the selection?

F Everyone likes blogs.

G Most blogs contain false information.

H Most blogs belong to individuals.

J Many people enjoy creating blogs.

29 Which would be an effective way to check the following statement of fact?

The computer program that is needed to create a blog is either free or very cheap.

A Consult an almanac.

B Look up *blog* in a dictionary.

C Read an article about interesting blogs.

D Interview a person who has created a blog.

30 What is the third paragraph mostly about?

F the history of blogging

G how quickly the number of blogs is growing

H the many uses of blogs

J why businesses support blogs

31 Look at the graph. What will probably happen when information for the next month is added?

A The line will go up sharply.

B The line will continue to be straight.

C The line will go down.

D The line will go all the way down to zero.

32 The title is "What's New on the Internet?" What is the best alternative title for the selection?

F "Eight Million and Counting"

G "The Basics of Blogging"

H "Just the Facts"

J "Dear Diary"

33 What was the author's main purpose for writing the selection?

A to convince readers to blog

B to discuss uses of the Internet

C to entertain readers with excerpts from blogs

D to explain the popularity of blogging

Directions

Write your answer to Question B on the lines below. Base your answer on "A Trip Back in Time" and "What's New on the Internet?"

B Think about Pang Chen's activities in "A Trip Back in Time" and the new popularity of blogging in "What's New on the Internet?" State one way in which leaving Chinese characters on a wall is similar to creating a blog. State one way in which leaving Chinese characters on a wall is different from creating a blog.

WRITING ACROSS TEXTS

_____

_____

_____

_____

_____

_____

_____

_____

_____

_____

PART 2: VOCABULARY

Directions
Mark your answer choice for Numbers 34 through 48.

34 "Working for the Future" tells about *unfair* child labor practices. In other words, the child labor practices are

F not fair.

G always fair.

H usually fair.

J sometimes fair.

35 What does *affected* mean in the following sentence?

Kielburger was affected by this stranger's difficult life, and he felt that he had to do something to try to change unfair labor practices in the world.

A temporarily amused

B seriously endangered

C emotionally moved

D permanently saddened

36 "Working for the Future" states that "When Kielburger speaks to youth groups, he tells them that even the smallest action can have an impact." Which of these is a synonym for *impact?*

F fullness

G challenge

H effect

J explanation

Use this entry from a dictionary to answer Numbers 37 and 38.

> **back** (bak), **1** *adv.* in the place from which something or someone came: *Please put the books back when you're finished.* **2** *n.* the part of a person's body opposite the front part of the body or face: *Mom put sunblock on Sally's back at the pool.* **3** *n.* the reverse, under, or wrong side: *We cleaned the back of the car.* **4** *v.* to support or help: *Many of her friends backed her plan.* **5** *adj.* behind in space or time: *Have you read the back issues of this magazine?*

37   **Which definition does *back* have in the following sentence?**

> *Some of these people were not allowed to enter the new homeland they had dreamed of and were sent back to China.*

A   definition 1

B   definition 2

C   definition 3

D   definition 4

38   **What part of speech is *back* in the following sentence?**

> *Some came because they couldn't make the back payments on their farms.*

F   verb

G   adjective

H   noun

J   adverb

39   **What does *influenced* mean in the following sentence?**

> *However, a park ranger found the poems and notes on the walls, and he organized a group of people who influenced the government to save the important buildings.*

A   asked

B   persuaded

C   commanded

D   pleaded with

40 Which of the following is a synonym for *recognize* as it is used in the following sentence?

> *Winsie did not recognize the Chinese characters, but her mother and father excitedly agreed that they spelled out "Pang Chen, 1930."*

F know

G study

H view

J touch

41 With the suffix *-ion* added to the base word, what does the word *confusion* mean?

A without being confused

B confused to a certain degree

C state or quality of being confused

D confused repeatedly

42 Which of the following guide words would appear on the dictionary page on which the word *detained* could be found?

F deny—dental

G describe—desert

H detect—dial

J destroy—devil

43 Which meaning of *article* is used in the following sentence?

> *When he was twelve years old, in 1995, Kielburger was searching for the comics page in the newspaper when he came upon an article about a twelve-year-old boy in Pakistan.*

A a factual story

B an item of goods

C a business matter

D a word used with a noun

44 What is a synonym for *instant* in the following sentence?

Blogging is also a way to give instant news on events while they are happening.

F immediate

G detailed

H brief

J accurate

45 Which of the following best explains the phrase *breaking news?*

A news with a negative impact

B news as events are happening

C news about not obeying the law

D news that is delivered in sections

46 Which of the following guide words would appear on the dictionary page on which the word *accurate* could be found?

F abandon—accident

G ache—actor

H accent—account

J accept—acid

47 Which two words have nearly the same meaning?

A *used* and *shared*

B *provide* and *know*

C *express* and *change*

D *created* and *made*

48 What is the base word of *combination?*

F combine

G comb

H nation

J bin

PART 3: WRITING CONVENTIONS

Directions
Mark your answer choice for Numbers 49 through 60.

49 The dog growled. What part of speech is the word *The?*

- **A** article
- **B** verb
- **C** adverb
- **D** noun

50 She turned <u>quickly</u>. What part of speech is the word *quickly?*

- **F** adjective
- **G** verb
- **H** adverb
- **J** noun

51 Loud music bothers my parents. What part of speech is the word *Loud?*

- **A** adverb
- **B** noun
- **C** pronoun
- **D** adjective

52 Which of the following sentences is written correctly?

- **F** My cousin came to visit, and we had fun.
- **G** My uncle sent a letter to she and I.
- **H** Him and me rode our bikes to school.
- **J** We will ride home from the party with they all.

53 Everyone cheered <u>when the team walked in</u>. What are the underlined words?

- **A** compound sentence
- **B** dependent clause
- **C** complex sentence
- **D** independent clause

54 Which sentence is written correctly?

F He sat the book on the table.

G He sit the book on the table.

H He set the book on the table.

J He setted the book on the table.

55 Which sentence is written correctly?

A Mark asked us "if we were ready to go home."

B Mom said "we can go to the park today."

C "Let's play kickball," Joan said.

D "How many people are coming? he asked."

56 Which sentence is written correctly?

F Elephants, and tigers are my favorite animals.

G He put strawberries, raspberries, and blackberries in the pie.

H Quinn will you carry this?

J We washed, dried, and brushed, the dog.

57 Which sentence is written correctly?

A They wants to join us.

B My brother climb trees.

C The girls walks to school.

D He reads a book every week.

58 Which sentence is written correctly?

F They know whom was at the gym.

G We wondered whom the gift was for.

H She asked, "Who was the call for?"

J "Whom did that?" he demanded.

59 **Which sentence is written correctly?**

  A Jon lives in Chester, Ohio.

  B Alice walked to the Library after school.

  C Mindy wants to go to Smith college next year.

  D Rudy lives on Main street.

60 **Which sentence is written correctly?**

  F I watched a flock of goose.

  G It took four mens to move the desk.

  H She has two tooths that are loose.

  J Seven children came to my party.

PART 4: WRITING

> ## PROMPT
>
> In "Working for the Future" and "A Trip Back in Time," both Craig Kielburger and a park ranger persuade others about a cause he feels is important. Think of a cause you feel strongly about and the reasons you support it. Write a persuasive essay to convince others to support your cause.

CHECKLIST FOR WRITERS

_____ Did I think about a cause for which I have strong feelings and why I believe this is a good cause?

_____ Did I take notes on the reasons others and I support this cause before I started writing?

_____ Did I organize my paper in a logical way?

_____ Did I use words and details that clearly expressed my ideas and will persuade others to support my cause?

_____ Do my sentences make sense?

_____ Did I check my sentences for proper grammar and punctuation?

_____ Did I check my spelling?

_____ Did I make sure my paper is the way I want readers to read it?